FAMOUS POEMS

AN ANTHOLOGY
OF THE FAVOURITE POEMS
OF ENGLISH VERSE

Compiled by

W. G. BEBBINGTON, M.A. (Oxon)

SCHOFIELD & SIMS LTD.
HUDDERSFIELD

FIRST PRINTED 1962

PRINTED IN ENGLAND BY
ALFRED JUBB & SON LTD.
HUDDERSFIELD

PREFACE

Plus ça change, plus c'est la même chose.

". . . such is the regularity with which 'new' anthologies roll off the presses that soon some publisher is going to find himself with a lawsuit on his hands for unwittingly reproducing a 'Wanderings in Arcadia' or a 'Charms of Poetry' that first came out in 1926."

—*Times Educational Supplement.*
9th October, 1960.

I doubt if there is any task which the English teacher dislikes more than the choosing of a 'new' anthology; for not only is the number of books enormous, but he will not be able to decide easily which is the best or even why any one of them is preferable to another. I am speaking of the so-called 'general' anthologies, though the specialised ones (comic, narrative, England, animals and so on) are also far too numerous and alike.

Why is the choice so difficult? Simply because every anthology is only a variation on the same old theme, a variation which there is no point in making. For the theme remains, it must remain, the same, and it is this theme that England's schoolchildren are expected to know: the famous, and usually short, poems, ranging from Elizabethan times to the twentieth century. 'Famous' is the vital word, not 'best', not even 'good'. These poems are the heritage, they are this England, and children should not leave school without knowing them. And every anthologist realises that he must include as many of them as possible, however much other material he may put in for desperate variation.

In this anthology, however, the theme stands alone; here, by themselves, are the old favourites. They are not quite all here perhaps, but most school anthologies are too big, and in any case, I have deliberately omitted the longer ones like 'The Ancient Mariner' which are better on their own. I have also deliberately not included extracts or pieces which, being modern, are not yet part of the heritage. For these 132 poems are the old favourites; indeed, the book is not a selection at all, it is a collection of the most anthologised

v

poems, every one of them in school-book after school-book, as respectable as the national anthem.

I offer this 'new' anthology, then, to the English teacher, who, if he accepts it in the spirit in which it is offered, will not have to make the old difficult choice and the old unnecessary decision.

W.G.B.

ACKNOWLEDGEMENTS

We are indebted to the following authors, executors and publishers for permission to include in this book the poems indicated:

The Soldier from "Collected Poems of Rupert Brooke" to Messrs. Sidgwick & Jackson Ltd.

The Old Ships from "Collected Poems of James Elroy Flecker" to Messrs. Martin Secker & Warburg Ltd., and Messrs. A. P. Watt & Son.

Into Battle by Julian Grenfell to Lady Salmond.

Lights Out by Edward Thomas to Mrs. H. Thomas.

Anthem for Doomed Youth by Wilfred Owen to Messrs. Chatto & Windus Ltd.

Weathers and **The Oxen** from "Collected Poems of Thomas Hardy" to the Trustees of the Hardy Estate and Messrs. Macmillan & Co. Ltd.

London Snow from "Shorter Poems of Robert Bridges" to The Clarendon Press, Oxford.

Snake from "The Complete Poems of D. H. Lawrence" to the Estate of the late Frieda Lawrence and Messrs. Laurence Pollinger Ltd.

The Ducks by Kenneth Grahame to Messrs. Curtis Brown Ltd.

Gunga Din from "Barrack Room Ballads", and **Recessional** from "The Five Nations" by Rudyard Kipling to Mrs. Bambridge, The Macmillan Co. of Canada, Messrs. Methuen & Co. Ltd., and Messrs. A. P. Watt & Son.

If from "Rewards and Fairies" by Rudyard Kipling to Mrs. Bambridge, Messrs. Macmillan & Co. Ltd., The Macmillan Co. of Canada and Messrs. A. P. Watt & Son.

The Donkey from "The Wild Knight and Other Poems" by G. K. Chesterton published by Messrs. J. M. Dent & Sons Ltd., to Miss D. E. Collins and Messrs. A. P. Watt & Son.

Loveliest of Trees and **When I was One-and-Twenty** from "Collected Poems of A. E. Housman", published by Messrs. Jonathan Cape Ltd., to the Society of Authors as the Literary representative of the Trustees of the Estate of the late A. E. Housman.

Vitai Lampada, Admirals All, Drake's Drum and **He Fell Among Thieves** from "Poems New and Old" by Sir Henry Newbolt, published by Messrs. John Murray Ltd., to Captain Francis Newbolt and Messrs. A. P. Watt & Son.

The Lake Isle of Innisfree from "Collected Poems of W. B. Yeats" to Mrs. Yeats, Messrs. Macmillan & Co. Ltd., and Messrs. A. P. Watt & Son.

Leisure from "Collected Poems of W. H. Davies" to Mrs. H. M. Davies and Messrs. Jonathan Cape Ltd.

For the Fallen by Laurence Binyon to Mrs. Cicely Binyon and the Society of Authors.

The South Country by Hilaire Belloc to A. D. Peters.

Romance from "The Hunter and Other Poems" by W. J. Turner to Messrs. Sidgwick & Jackson Ltd.

The Highwayman by Alfred Noyes to Messrs. William Blackwood & Sons Ltd.

vii

The Listeners and **The Scarecrow** by Walter de la Mare to the Literary Trustees of Walter de la Mare and the Society of Authors.

Mrs. Reece Laughs by Martin Armstrong to Messrs. Martin Secker & Warburg Ltd. and A. D. Peters.

Night Mail by W. H. Auden to H.M. Postmaster General.

Macavity, the Mystery Cat from "Old Possum's Book of Practical Cats" and **Journey of the Magi** from "Collected Poems" by T. S. Eliot to Messrs. Faber & Faber Ltd.

Flannan Isle by Wilfred Gibson and **Time, You old Gipsy Man** from "Poems" by Ralph Hodgson to Messrs. Macmillan & Co. Ltd.

Cargoes, Sea-Fever and **Roadways** by John Masefield to Dr. John Masefield, O.M., the Society of Authors and The Macmillan Co., New York.

CONTENTS

			Page
1.	The Passionate Shepherd to his Love	*Christopher Marlowe*	13
2.	Spring	*Thomas Nashe*	14
3.	Under the Greenwood Tree	*William Shakespeare*	14
4.	Blow, blow, thou Winter Wind	,, ,,	15
5.	O Mistress Mine	,, ,,	16
6.	Come Away, Come Away, Death	,, ,,	16
7.	Fear No More the Heat o' the Sun	,, ,,	17
8.	It was a Lover and his Lass	,, ,,	18
9.	Who is Silvia?	,, ,,	19
10.	To Celia	*Ben Jonson*	19
11.	The Character of a Happy Life	*Sir Henry Wotton*	20
12.	To Lucasta, Going to the Wars	*Richard Lovelace*	21
13.	To Althea, from Prison	,, ,,	22
14.	Death the Leveller	*James Shirley*	23
15.	Gather ye Rose-buds	*Robert Herrick*	23
16.	To Daffodils	,, ,,	24
17.	Sonnet on his Blindness	*John Milton*	25
18.	On a Girdle	*Edmund Waller*	25
19.	Go, Lovely Rose	,, ,,	26
20.	The Blind Boy	*Colley Cibber*	26
21.	How Sleep the Brave	*William Collins*	27
22.	Ode on the Death of a Favourite Cat, Drowned in a Tub of Goldfishes	*Thomas Gray*	28
23.	Elegy on the Death of a Mad Dog	*Oliver Goldsmith*	29
24.	My Love is like a Red, Red Rose	*Robert Burns*	30
25.	A Man's a Man for a' That	,, ,,	31
26.	Auld Lang Syne	,, ,,	32
27.	The Loss of the 'Royal George'	*William Cowper*	33
28.	La Belle Dame Sans Merci	*John Keats*	34
29.	To Autumn	,, ,,	36
30.	Meg Merrilies	,, ,,	37
31.	On First Looking into Chapman's Homer	,, ,,	39
32.	Ozymandias	*P. B. Shelley*	39
33.	The Cloud	,, ,,	40
34.	To a Skylark	,, ,,	42
35.	The Burial of Sir John Moore	*Charles Wolfe*	45
36.	The Destruction of Sennacherib	*Lord Byron*	46

37.	So, We'll Go no more A-Roving	*Lord Byron*	47
38.	She Walks in Beauty	,, ,,	48
39.	The Lamb	*William Blake*	49
40.	The Tyger	,, ,,	49
41.	Jerusalem	,, ,,	50
42.	Young Lochinvar	*Sir Walter Scott*	51
43.	Pibroch of Donuil Dhu	,, ,,	52
44.	Jock of Hazeldean	,, ,,	54
45.	Kubla Khan	*S. T. Coleridge*	55
46.	A Sea Song	*Alan Cunningham*	56
47.	The Inchcape Rock	*Robert Southey*	57
48.	After Blenheim	,, ,,	59
49.	Bishop Hatto	,, ,,	61
50.	Hohenlinden	*Thomas Campbell*	64
51.	Ye Mariners of England	,, ,,	65
52.	The Song of the Shirt	*Thomas Hood*	67
53.	I remember, I remember	,, ,,	70
54.	Remembrance	*Emily Brontë*	71
55.	Composed upon Westminster Bridge, Sept. 3, 1802	*William Wordsworth*	72
56.	The Solitary Reaper	,, ,,	72
57.	The Daffodils	,, ,,	73
58.	To the Cuckoo	,, ,,	74
59.	Abou Ben Adhem	*Leigh Hunt*	75
60.	How do I Love Thee?	*Elizabeth Barrett Browning*	76
61.	Say Not the Struggle Naught Availeth	*A. H. Clough*	76
62.	Little Trotty Wagtail	*John Clare*	77
63.	The War Song of Dinas Vawr	*T. L. Peacock*	78
64.	The Three Men of Gotham	,, ,,	79
65.	The Knight's Leap	*Charles Kingsley*	80
66.	The Sands of Dee	,, ,,	81
67.	Requiescat	*Matthew Arnold*	82
68.	Dover Beach	,, ,,	82
69.	The Jumblies	*Edward Lear*	84
70.	The Pelican Chorus	,, ,,	86
71.	The Owl and the Pussy-Cat	,, ,,	89
72.	Home-thoughts from Abroad	*Robert Browning*	90
73.	How They Brought the Good News from Ghent to Aix	,, ,,	90
74.	Incident of the French Camp	,, ,,	92
75.	Prospice	,, ,,	94
76.	Pied Beauty	*Gerard Manley Hopkins*	95

			Page
77.	The Fairies	*William Allingham*	95
78.	Heraclitus	*W. J. Cory*	97
79.	The Charge of the Light Brigade	*Lord Tennyson*	97
80.	The Lady of Shalott	,, ,,	99
81.	The Splendour Falls on Castle Walls	,, ,,	103
82.	The Eagle	,, ,,	104
83.	Break, Break, Break	,, ,,	104
84.	The Brook	,, ,,	105
85.	Crossing the Bar	,, ,,	107
86.	Up-Hill	*Christina Rossetti*	107
87.	Sing me a Song of a Lad that is Gone	*R. L. Stevenson*	108
88.	Requiem	,, ,,	109
89.	The High Tide on the Coast of Lincolnshire (1571)	*Jean Ingelow*	110
90.	He Thought he Saw	*Lewis Carroll*	115
91.	Father William	,, ,,	116
92.	The Walrus and the Carpenter	,, ,,	118
93.	Out of the Night that Covers Me	*W. E. Henley*	121
94.	In No Strange Land	*Francis Thompson*	122
95.	A Runnable Stag	*John Davidson*	123
96.	The Soldier	*Rupert Brooke*	125
97.	The Old Ships	*James Elroy Flecker*	126
98.	Into Battle	*Julian Grenfell*	127
99.	Lights Out	*Edward Thomas*	128
100.	Anthem for Doomed Youth	*Wilfred Owen*	129
101.	Weathers	*Thomas Hardy*	130
102.	The Oxen	,, ,,	130
103.	London Snow	*Robert Bridges*	131
104.	Snake	*D. H. Lawrence*	132
105.	The Ducks	*Kenneth Grahame*	135
106.	Gunga Din	*Rudyard Kipling*	136
107.	Recessional	,, ,,	138
108.	If—	,, ,,	139
109.	The Donkey	*G. K. Chesterton*	140
110.	Loveliest of Trees	*A. E. Housman*	141
111.	When I was One-and-Twenty	,, ,,	141
112.	Vitaï Lampada	*Sir Henry Newbolt*	142
113.	Admirals All	,, ,,	143
114.	Drake's Drum	,, ,,	145
115.	He Fell among Thieves	,, ,,	146
116.	The Lake Isle of Innisfree	*W. B. Yeats*	147

			Page
117.	Leisure	*W. H. Davies*	148
118.	For the Fallen	*Laurence Binyon*	149
119.	The South Country	*Hilaire Belloc*	150
120.	Romance	*W. J. Turner*	152
121.	The Highwayman	*Alfred Noyes*	153
122.	The Listeners	*Walter de la Mare*	157
123.	The Scarecrow	,, ,, ,,	158
124.	Mrs. Reece Laughs	*Martin Armstrong*	158
125.	Night Mail	*W. H. Auden*	159
126.	Macavity: the Mystery Cat	*T. S. Eliot*	161
127.	Journey of the Magi	,, ,,	162
128.	Flannan Isle	*W. W. Gibson*	163
129.	Time, You old Gipsy Man	*Ralph Hodgson*	167
130.	Cargoes	*John Masefield*	168
131.	Sea-Fever	,, ,,	168
132.	Roadways	,, ,,	169

1 THE PASSIONATE SHEPHERD TO HIS LOVE

Christopher Marlowe
(1564-1593)

Come live with me, and be my love,
And we will all the pleasures prove
That valleys, groves, hills and fields,
Woods, or steepy mountain yields.

And we will sit upon the rocks,
Seeing the shepherds feed their flocks
By shallow rivers, to whose falls
Melodious birds sing madrigals.

And I will make thee beds of roses
And a thousand fragrant posies,
A cap of flowers, and a kirtle
Embroidered all with leaves of myrtle.

A gown made of the finest wool
Which from our pretty lambs we pull,
Fair lined slippers for the cold
With buckles of the purest gold.

A belt of straw and ivy buds
With coral clasps and amber studs;
And if these pleasures may thee move,
Come live with me, and be my love.

The shepherd swains shall dance and sing
For thy delight each May-morning.
If these delights thy mind may move,
Then live with me, and be my love.

2 SPRING

Thomas Nashe
(1567-1601)

Spring, the sweet Spring, is the year's pleasant king;
Then blooms each thing, then maids dance in a ring,
Cold doth not sting, the pretty birds do sing,—
Cuckoo, jug-jug, pu-we, to-witta-woo!

The palm and may make country houses gay,
Lambs frisk and play, the shepherds pipe all day,
And we hear aye birds tune this merry lay,—
Cuckoo, jug-jug, pu-we, to-witta-woo!

The fields breathe sweet, the daisies kiss our feet,
Young lovers meet, old wives a-sunning sit,
In every street these tunes our ears do greet,—
Cuckoo, jug-jug, pu-we, to-witta-woo!
Spring! the sweet Spring!

3 UNDER THE GREENWOOD TREE

William Shakespeare
(1564-1616)

Under the greenwood tree,
Who loves to lie with me,
And tune his merry note
Unto the sweet bird's throat,
Come hither, come hither, come hither:
Here shall he see
No enemy
But winter and rough weather.

Who doth ambition shun,
And loves to live i' the sun,
Seeking the food he eats,
And pleased with what he gets,
Come hither, come hither, come hither:
Here shall he see
No enemy
But winter and rough weather.

4 BLOW, BLOW, THOU WINTER WIND

William Shakespeare

Blow, blow, thou winter wind,
Thou art not so unkind
As man's ingratitude;
Thy tooth is not so keen,
Because thou art not seen,
Although thy breath be rude.
Heigh ho! sing heigh ho! unto the green holly:
Most friendship is feigning, most loving mere folly:
Then heigh ho, the holly!
This life is most jolly.

Freeze, freeze, thou bitter sky,
Thou dost not bite so nigh
As benefits forgot:
Though thou the waters warp,
Thy sting is not so sharp
As friend remember'd not.
Heigh ho! sing heigh ho! unto the green holly:
Most friendship is feigning, most loving mere folly:
Then heigh ho, the holly!
This life is most jolly.

5   O MISTRESS MINE

William Shakespeare

O mistress mine, where are you roaming?
O, stay and hear; your true-love's coming,
    That can sing both high and low:
Trip no further, pretty sweeting;
Journeys end in lovers' meeting,
    Every wise man's son doth know.

What is love? 'tis not hereafter;
Present mirth hath present laughter;
    What's to come is still unsure:
In delay there lies no plenty;
Then come kiss me, sweet-and-twenty,
    Youth's a stuff will not endure.

6   COME AWAY, COME AWAY, DEATH

William Shakespeare

Come away, come away, death,
    And in sad cypress let me be laid;
Fly away, fly away, breath;
    I am slain by a fair cruel maid.
My shroud of white, stuck all with yew,
    O, prepare it!
My part of death, no one so true
    Did share it.

Not a flower, not a flower sweet,
    On my black coffin let there be strown;
Not a friend, not a friend greet
    My poor corse, where my bones shall be thrown:
A thousand thousand sighs to save,
        Lay me, O, where
Sad true lover never find my grave,
        To weep there!

7   FEAR NO MORE THE HEAT O' THE SUN

William Shakespeare

Fear no more the heat o' the sun,
    Nor the furious winter's rages;
Thou thy worldly task hast done,
    Home art gone, and ta'en thy wages:
Golden lads and girls all must,
As chimney-sweepers, come to dust.

Fear no more the frown o' the great,
    Thou art past the tyrant's stroke;
Care no more to clothe and eat;
    To thee the reed is as the oak:
The sceptre, learning, physic, must
All follow this, and come to dust.

Fear no more the lightning-flash
    Nor the all-dreaded thunder-stone;
Fear not slander, censure rash;
    Thou hast finish'd joy and moan:
All lovers young, all lovers must
Consign to thee, and come to dust.

No exorciser harm thee!
  Nor no witchcraft charm thee!
Ghost unlaid forbear thee!
  Nothing ill come near thee!
Quiet consummation have;
And renowned be thy grave!

8 IT WAS A LOVER AND HIS LASS

William Shakespeare

It was a lover and his lass,
  With a hey, and a ho, and a hey nonino,
That o'er the green corn-field did pass,
  In spring time, the only pretty ring-time,
  When birds do sing, hey ding a ding, ding;
  Sweet lovers love the spring.

Between the acres of the rye,
  With a hey, and a ho, and a hey nonino,
These pretty country-folks would lie,
  In spring time, the only pretty ring-time,
  When birds do sing, hey ding a ding, ding;
  Sweet lovers love the spring.

This carol they began that hour,
  With a hey, and a ho, and a hey nonino,
How that life was but a flower,
  In spring time, the only pretty ring-time,
  When birds do sing, hey ding a ding, ding;
  Sweet lovers love the spring.

And, therefore, take the present time,
  With a hey, and a ho, and a hey nonino,
For love is crowned with the prime
  In spring time, the only pretty ring-time,
  When birds do sing, hey ding a ding, ding;
  Sweet lovers love the spring.

9 WHO IS SILVIA?

William Shakespeare

Who is Silvia?   What is she?
  That all our swains commend her?
Holy, fair, and wise is she;
  The heaven such grace did lend her,
That she might admired be.

Is she kind as she is fair?
  For beauty lives with kindness:
Love doth to her eyes repair,
  To help him of his blindness;
And, being help'd, inhabits there.

Then to Silvia let us sing,
  That Silvia is excelling;
She excels each mortal thing
  Upon the dull earth dwelling:
To her let us garlands bring.

10 TO CELIA

Ben Jonson
(1572-1637)

Drink to me only with thine eyes,
  And I will pledge with mine;
Or leave a kiss but in the cup
  And I'll not look for wine.
The thirst that from the soul doth rise
  Doth ask a drink divine;
But might I of Jove's nectar sup,
  I would not change for thine.

I sent thee late a rosy wreath,
Not so much honouring thee
As giving it a hope that there
It could not wither'd be;
But thou thereon didst only breathe,
And sent'st it back to me;
Since when it grows, and smells, I swear,
Not of itself but thee!

11   THE CHARACTER OF A HAPPY LIFE

Sir Henry Wotton
(1568-1639)

How happy is he born or taught
That serveth not another's will;
Whose armour is his honest thought,
And simple truth his utmost skill!

Whose passions not his masters are;
Whose soul is still prepared for death,
Untied unto the world by care
Of public fame or private breath;

Who envies none that chance doth raise,
Nor vice; who never understood
How deepest wounds are given by praise;
Nor rules of state, but rules of good;

Who hath his life from rumours freed;
Whose conscience is his strong retreat;
Whose state can neither flatterers feed,
Nor ruin make oppressors great;

Who God doth late and early pray
 More of His grace than gifts to lend;
And entertains the harmless day
 With a religious book or friend;

This man is freed from servile bands
 Of hope to rise or fear to fall:
Lord of himself, though not of lands,
 And having nothing, yet hath all.

12 TO LUCASTA, GOING TO THE WARS

Richard Lovelace
(1618-1658)

Tell me not, Sweet, I am unkind,
 That from the nunnery
Of thy chaste breast, and quiet mind,
 To war and arms I fly.

True; a new mistress now I chase,
 The first foe in the field;
And with a stronger faith embrace
 A sword, a horse, a shield.

Yet this inconstancy is such
 As thou too shalt adore;
I could not love thee, Dear, so much,
 Loved I not Honour more.

13   TO ALTHEA, FROM PRISON

Richard Lovelace

When Love with unconfined wings
    Hovers within my gates,
And my divine Althea brings
    To whisper at the grates;
When I lie tangled in her hair,
    And fetter'd to her eye,
The Gods, that wanton in the air,
    Know no such liberty.

When flowing cups run swiftly round
    With no allaying Thames,
Our careless heads with roses bound,
    Our hearts with loyal flames;
When thirsty grief in wine we steep,
    When healths and draughts go free,
Fishes that tipple in the deep,
    Know no such liberty.

When, like committed linnets, I
    With shriller throat shall sing
The sweetness, mercy, majesty,
    And glories of my King;
When I shall voice aloud, how good
    He is, how great should be,
Enlarged winds, that curl the flood,
    Know no such liberty.

Stone walls do not a prison make,
    Nor iron bars a cage;
Minds innocent and quiet take
    That for an hermitage;
If I have freedom in my love,
    And in my soul am free;
Angels alone that soar above,
    Enjoy such liberty.

14 DEATH THE LEVELLER

James Shirley
(1596-1666)

The glories of our blood and state
    Are shadows, not substantial things;
There is no armour against Fate;
    Death lays his icy hand on kings:
        Sceptre and Crown
        Must tumble down,
And in the dust be equal made
With the poor crooked scythe and spade.

Some men with swords may reap the field,
    And plant fresh laurels where they kill:
But their strong nerves at last must yield;
    They tame but one another still:
        Early or late
        They stoop to fate,
And must give up their murmuring breath
When they, pale captives, creep to death.

The garlands wither on your brow;
    Then boast no more your mighty deeds!
Upon Death's purple altar now
    See where the victor-victim bleeds.
        Your heads must come
        To the cold tomb;
Only the actions of the just
Smell sweet, and blossom in their dust.

15 GATHER YE ROSE-BUDS

Robert Herrick
(1591-1674)

Gather ye rose-buds while ye may,
    Old Time is still a-flying:
And this same flower that smiles to-day
    To-morrow will be dying.

The glorious lamp of heaven, the sun,
    The higher he's a-getting
The sooner will his race be run,
    And nearer he's to setting.

That age is best which is the first,
    When youth and blood are warmer:
But being spent, the worse, and worst
    Times, still succeed the former.

Then be not coy, but use your time;
    And while ye may, go marry:
For having lost but once your prime,
    You may for ever tarry.

16   TO DAFFODILS

Robert Herrick

Fair Daffodils, we weep to see
    You haste away so soon:
As yet the early-rising sun
        Has not attain'd his noon.
            Stay, stay
        Until the hasting day
            Has run
        But to the evensong;
And, having pray'd together, we
    Will go with you along.

We have short time to stay, as you,
    We have as short a spring;
As quick a growth to meet decay,
        As you, or anything.
            We die,
        As your hours do, and dry
            Away
        Like to the summer's rain;
Or as the pearls of morning's dew,
    Ne'er to be found again.

17 SONNET ON HIS BLINDNESS

John Milton
(1608-1674)

When I consider how my light is spent,
  Ere half my days, in this dark world and wide,
  And that one talent which is death to hide,
  Lodg'd with me useless, though my soul more bent
To serve therewith my Maker, and present
  My true account, lest He returning chide,
  Doth God exact day-labour, light deny'd,
  I fondly ask; But patience to prevent
That murmur, soon replies, God doth not need
  Either man's work or His own gifts, who best
  Bear His mild yoke, they serve Him best, His state
Is kingly. Thousands at His bidding speed
  And post o'er Land and Ocean without rest:
  They also serve who only stand and wait.

18 ON A GIRDLE

Edmund Waller
(1606-1687)

That which her slender waist confin'd
Shall now my joyful temples bind;
No monarch but would give his crown
His arms might do what this has done.

It was my Heaven's extremest sphere,
The pale which held that lovely deer:
My joy, my grief, my hope, my love,
Did all within this circle move.

A narrow compass! and yet there
Dwelt all that's good, and all that's fair!
Give me but what this ribband bound,
Take all the rest the sun goes round!

19   GO, LOVELY ROSE

Edmund Waller

Go, lovely Rose!
Tell her, that wastes her time and me,
   That now she knows,
When I resemble her to thee,
How sweet and fair she seems to be.

Tell her that's young,
And shuns to have her graces spied,
   That hadst thou sprung
In deserts where no men abide,
Thou must have uncommended died.

Small is the worth
Of beauty from the light retired:
   Bid her come forth,
Suffer herself to be desired,
And not blush so to be admired.

Then die—that she
The common fate of all things rare
   May read in thee:
How small a part of time they share
That are so wondrous sweet and fair!

20   THE BLIND BOY

Colley Cibber
(1671-1757)

O say, what is that thing called Light,
   Which I must ne'er enjoy?
What are the blessings of the sight?
   O tell your poor blind boy!

You talk of wondrous things you see;
    You say the sun shines bright;
I feel him warm, but how can he
    Or make it day or night?

My day or night myself I make
    Whene'er I sleep or play;
And could I ever keep awake,
    With me 'twere always day.

With heavy sighs I often hear
    You mourn my hapless woe;
But sure with patience I can bear
    A loss I ne'er can know.

Then let not what I cannot have
    My cheer of mind destroy:
Whilst thus I sing, I am a king,
    Although a poor blind boy.

21   HOW SLEEP THE BRAVE

William Collins
(1721-1759)

How sleep the brave who sink to rest
By all their country's wishes blest!
When Spring, with dewy fingers cold,
Returns to deck their hallow'd mould,
She there shall dress a sweeter sod
Than fancy's feet have ever trod.

By fairy hands their knell is rung,
By forms unseen their dirge is sung;
There honour comes, a pilgrim grey,
To bless the turf that wraps their clay,—
And freedom shall awhile repair,
To dwell, a weeping hermit, there!

22 ODE ON THE DEATH OF A FAVOURITE CAT, DROWNED IN A TUB OF GOLDFISHES

Thomas Gray
(1716-1771)

'Twas on a lofty vase's side,
Where China's gayest art had dyed
    The azure flowers that blow:
Demurest of the tabby kind,
The pensive Selima reclined,
    Gazed on the lake below.

Her conscious tail her joy declared:
The fair round face, the snowy beard,
    The velvet of her paws,
Her coat, that with the tortoise vies,
Her ears of jet, and emerald eyes,
    She saw; and purred applause.

Still had she gazed; but 'midst the tide
Two angel forms were seen to glide,
    The Genii of the stream:
Their scaly armour's Tyrian hue
Through richest purple to the view
    Betrayed a golden gleam.

The hapless Nymph with wonder saw:
A whisker first and then a claw,
    With many an ardent wish,
She stretched in vain to reach the prize.
What female heart can gold despise?
    What cat's averse to fish?

Presumptuous maid! with looks intent
Again she stretched, again she bent,
    Nor knew the gulf between.
(Malignant Fate sat by, and smiled.)
The slippery verge her feet beguiled;
    She tumbled headlong in.

Eight times emerging from the flood
She mewed to ev'ry wat'ry god,
    Some speedy aid to send.
No Dolphin came, no Nereid stirred,
Nor cruel Tom, nor Susan heard—
    A fav'rite has no friend!

From hence, ye Beauties, undeceived,
Know, one false step is ne'er retrieved,
    And be with caution bold.
Not all that tempts your wand'ring eyes
And heedless hearts, is lawful prize,
    Nor all, that glisters, gold.

23   ELEGY ON THE DEATH OF A MAD DOG

Oliver Goldsmith
(1730-1774)

Good people all, of every sort,
    Give ear unto my song;
And if you find it wondrous short,
    It cannot hold you long.

In Islington there was a man,
    Of whom the world might say,
That still a godly race he ran,
    Whene'er he went to pray.

A kind and gentle heart he had,
    To comfort friends and foes;
The naked every day he clad,
    When he put on his clothes.

And in that town a dog was found,
    As many dogs there be,
Both mongrel, puppy, whelp, and hound,
    And curs of low degree.

This dog and man at first were friends;
    But when a pique began,
The dog, to gain his private ends,
    Went mad and bit the man.

Around from all the neighbouring streets,
    The wondering neighbours ran,
And swore the dog had lost his wits,
    To bite so good a man.

The wound it seemed both sore and sad
    To every Christian eye;
And while they swore the dog was mad,
    They swore the man would die.

But soon a wonder came to light,
    That showed the rogues they lied;
The man recovered of the bite,
    The dog it was that died.

24 O, MY LUVE IS LIKE A RED, RED ROSE

Robert Burns
(1759-1796)

My luve is like a red, red rose
    That's newly sprung in June:
My luve is like the melodie
    That's sweetly play'd in tune!

As fair art thou, my bonnie lass,
    So deep in luve am I:
And I will luve thee still, my dear,
    Till a' the seas gang dry:

Till a' the seas gang dry, my dear,
    And the rocks melt wi' the sun;
And I will luve thee still, my dear,
    While the sands o' life shall run.

And fare-thee-weel, my only luve!
  And fare-thee-weel, a while!
And I will come again, my luve,
  Tho' it were ten thousand mile!

25 A MAN'S A MAN FOR A' THAT

Robert Burns

Is there for honest Poverty
  That hings his head, an' a' that;
The coward slave—we pass him by,
  We dare be poor for a' that!
For a' that, an' a' that,
  Our toils obscure, an' a' that,
The rank is but the guinea's stamp,
  The Man's the gowd for a' that.

What though on hamely fare we dine,
  Wear hoddin gray, an' a' that;
Gie fools their silks, and knaves their wine,
  A Man's a Man for a' that:
For a' that, an' a' that,
  Their tinsel show, an' a' that;
The honest man, tho' e'er sae poor,
  Is king o' men for a' that.

Ye see yon birkie ca'd "a lord",
  Wha struts, an' stares, an' a' that;
Tho' hundreds worship at his word,
  He's but a coof for a' that:
For a' that, an' a' that,
  His riband, star, an' a' that;
The man o' independent mind
  He looks an' laughs at a' that.

A prince can mak a belted knight,
  A marquis, duke, an' a' that;
But an honest man's aboon his might,
  Gude faith, he mauna fa' that!
For a' that, an' a' that,
  Their dignities, an' a' that;
The pith o' sense, an' pride o' worth,
  Are higher rank than a' that.

Then let us pray that come it may
  (As come it will for a' that)
That Sense and Worth o'er a' the earth
  Shall bear the gree, an' a' that.
For a' that, an' a' that,
  It's coming yet, for a' that,
That Man to Man, the world o'er,
  Shall brothers be for a' that.

26   AULD LANG SYNE

Robert Burns

Should auld acquaintance be forgot,
  And never brought to mind?
Should auld acquaintance be forgot,
  And days o' lang syne?

Chorus—For auld lang syne, my dear,
      For auld lang syne,
    We'll tak a cup o' kindness yet,
      For auld lang syne.

And surely ye'll be your pint stowp!
  And surely I'll be mine!
And we'll tak a cup o' kindness yet,
  For auld lang syne.
      For auld, etc.

We twa hae run about the braes,
    And pou'd the gowans fine;
But we've wander'd mony a weary fit,
    Sin' auld lang syne.
        For auld, etc.

We twa hae paidl'd in the burn,
    Frae morning sun till dine;
But seas between us braid hae roar'd
    Sin' auld lang syne.
        For auld, etc.

And here's a hand, my trusty fiere!
    And gie's a hand o' thine!
And we'll tak a right gude willie-waught,
    For auld lang syne.
        For auld etc.

27   THE LOSS OF THE 'ROYAL GEORGE'

William Cowper
(1731-1800)

Toll for the brave!
    The brave that are no more!
All sunk beneath the wave,
    Fast by their native shore!

Eight hundred of the brave,
    Whose courage well was tried,
Had made the vessel heel,
    And laid her on her side.

A land-breeze shook the shrouds,
    And she was overset;
Down went the *Royal George*,
    With all her crew complete.

Toll for the brave!
    Brave Kempenfelt is gone;
His last sea-fight is fought;
    His work of glory done.

It was not in the battle,
    No tempest gave the shock;
She sprang no fatal leak;
    She ran upon no rock.

His sword was in its sheath;
    His fingers held the pen,
When Kempenfelt went down,
    With twice four hundred men.

Weigh the vessel up,
    Once dreaded by our foes!
And mingle with your cup
    The tears that England owes.

Her timbers yet are sound,
    And she may float again,
Full charged with England's thunder,
    And plough the distant main.

But Kempenfelt is gone,
    His victories are o'er;
And he and his eight hundred
    Shall plough the wave no more.

28   LA BELLE DAME SANS MERCI

John Keats
(1795-1821)

"O what can ail thee, knight-at-arms,
    Alone and palely loitering?
The sedge is wither'd from the lake,
    And no birds sing.

"O what can ail thee, knight-at-arms,
    So haggard and so woe-begone?
The squirrel's granary is full,
    And the harvest's done.

"I see a lily on thy brow,
    With anguish moist and fever dew,
And on thy cheeks a fading rose
    Fast withereth too."

"I met a lady in the meads
    Full beautiful—a faery's child;
Her hair was long, her foot was light,
    And her eyes were wild.

"I made a garland for her head,
    And bracelets too, and fragrant zone;
She look'd at me as she did love,
    And made sweet moan.

"I set her on my pacing steed
    And nothing else saw all day long;
For sideways would she bend, and sing
    A faery's song.

"She found me roots of relish sweet,
And honey wild, and manna dew,
    And sure in language strange she said,
    'I love thee true.'

"She took me to her elfin grot,
    And there she wept, and sigh'd full sore,
And there I shut her wild, wild eyes
    With kisses four.

"And there she lulled me asleep,
    And there I dreamed,—Ah! woe betide,
The latest dream I ever dream'd
    On the cold hill side.

"I saw pale kings, and princes too,
    Pale warriors, death-pale were they all;
They cried—'La belle Dame sans Merci
    Hath thee in thrall!'

"I saw their starv'd lips in the gloam
    With horrid warning gaped wide,
And I awoke, and found me here
    On the cold hill side.

"And this is why I sojourn here
    Alone and palely loitering,
Though the sedge is wither'd from the lake
    And no birds sing."

29   TO AUTUMN

John Keats

Season of mists and mellow fruitfulness,
    Close bosom-friend of the maturing sun;
Conspiring with him how to load and bless
    With fruit the vines that round the thatch-eaves run;
To bend with apples the moss'd cottage-trees,
    And fill all fruit with ripeness to the core;
        To swell the gourd, and plump the hazel shells
    With a sweet kernel; to set budding more,
And still more, later flowers for the bees,
Until they think warm days will never cease,
    For summer has o'erbrimm'd their clammy cells.

Who hath not seen thee oft amid thy store?
  Sometimes whoever seeks abroad may find
Thee sitting careless on a granary floor,
  Thy hair soft-lifted by the winnowing wind;
Or on a half-reap'd furrow sound asleep,
  Drowsed with the fume of poppies, while thy hook
    Spares the next swath and all its twined flowers:
And sometimes like a gleaner thou dost keep
Steady thy laden head across a brook;
Or by a cider-press, with patient look,
  Thou watchest the last oozings hours by hours.

Where are the songs of Spring? Aye, where are they?
  Think not of them, thou hast thy music too,—
While barred clouds bloom the soft-dying day,
  And touch the stubble-plains with rosy hue;
Then in a wailful choir the small gnats mourn
  Among the river-sallows, borne aloft
    Or sinking as the light wind lives or dies;
And full-grown lambs loud bleat from hilly bourn;
Hedge-crickets sing; and now with treble soft
The redbreast whistles from a garden-croft;
  And gathering swallows twitter in the skies.

30   MEG MERRILIES

John Keats

Old Meg she was a gipsy,
  And lived upon the moors:
Her bed it was the brown heath turf,
  And her house was out of doors.

Her apples were swart blackberries,
    Her currants pods o' broom;
Her wine was dew of the wild white rose,
    Her book a churchyard tomb.

Her brothers were the craggy hills,
    Her sisters larchen trees,—
Alone with her great family
    She lived as she did please.

No breakfast had she many a morn,
    No dinner many a noon,
And 'stead of supper she would stare
    Full hard against the moon.

But every morn of woodbine fresh
    She made her garlanding,
And every night the dark glen yew
    She wove, and she would sing.

And with her fingers, old and brown,
    She plaited mats o' rushes,
And gave them to the cottagers
    She met among the bushes.

Old Meg was brave as Margaret Queen,
    And tall as Amazon:
An old red blanket cloak she wore;
    A chip hat had she on.
God rest her agèd bones somewhere—
    She died full long agone!

31 ON FIRST LOOKING INTO
CHAPMAN'S HOMER

John Keats

Much have I travell'd in the realms of gold,
   And many goodly states and kingdoms seen;
   Round many western islands have I been
Which bards in fealty to Apollo hold.
Oft of one wide expanse had I been told
   That deep-brow'd Homer ruled as his demesne;
   Yet did I never breathe its pure serene
Till I heard Chapman speak out loud and bold:
Then felt I like some watcher of the skies
   When a new planet swims into his ken;
Or like stout Cortez when with eagle eyes
   He stared at the Pacific—and all his men
Look'd at each other with a wild surmise—
   Silent, upon a peak in Darien.

32 OZYMANDIAS

P. B. Shelley
(1792-1822)

I met a traveller from an antique land
Who said: Two vast and trunkless legs of stone
Stand in the desert.   Near them, on the sand,
Half sunk, a shatter'd visage lies, whose frown,
And wrinkled lip, and sneer of cold command,
Tell that its sculptor well those passions read
Which yet survive, stamp'd on these lifeless things,
The hand that mock'd them and the heart that fed:
And on the pedestal these words appear:
'My name is Ozymandias, king of kings:
Look on my works, ye Mighty, and despair!'
Nothing beside remains.   Round the decay
Of that colossal wreck, boundless and bare
The lone and level sands stretch far away.

THE CLOUD

P. B. Shelley •

I bring fresh showers for the thirsting flowers,
 From the seas and the streams;
I bear light shade for the leaves when laid
 In their noonday dreams.
From my wings are shaken the dews that waken
 The sweet buds every one,
When rocked to rest on their mother's breast,
 As she dances about the sun.
I wield the flail of the lashing hail,
 And whiten the green plains under,
And then again I dissolve it in rain,
 And laugh as I pass in thunder.

I sift the snow on the mountains below,
 And their great pines groan aghast;
And all the night 'tis my pillow white,
 While I sleep in the arms of the blast.
Sublime on the towers of my skiey bowers,
 Lightning my pilot sits;
In a cavern under is fettered the thunder,
 It struggles and howls at fits;
Over earth and ocean, with gentle motion,
 This pilot is guiding me,
Lured by the love of the genii that move
 In the depths of the purple sea;
Over the rills, and the crags, and the hills,
 Over the lakes and the plains,
Wherever he dream, under mountain or stream,
 The Spirit he loves remains;
And I all the while bask in heaven's blue smile,
 Whilst he is dissolving in rains.

The sanguine sunrise, with his meteor eyes,
    And his burning plumes outspread,
Leaps on the back of my sailing rack,
    When the morning star shines dead;
As on the jag of a mountain crag,
    Which an earthquake rocks and swings,
An eagle alit one moment may sit
    In the light of its golden wings.
And when sunset may breathe, from the lit sea beneath,
    Its ardours of rest and of love,
And the crimson pall of eve may fall
    From the depths of heaven above,
With wings folded I rest, on mine aery nest,
    As still as a brooding dove.

That orbèd maiden with white fire laden,
    Whom mortals call the moon,
Glides glimmering o'er my fleece-like floor,
    By the midnight breezes strewn;
And wherever the beat of her unseen feet,
    Which only the angels hear,
May have broken the woof of my tent's thin roof,
    The stars peep behind her and peer;
And I laugh to see them whirl and flee,
    Like a swarm of golden bees,
When I widen the rent in my wind-built tent,
    Till the calm rivers, lakes and seas,
Like strips of the sky fallen through me on high,
    Are each paved with the moon and these.

I bind the sun's throne with a burning zone,
    And the moon's with a girdle of pearl;
The volcanoes are dim, and the stars reel and swim,
    When the whirlwinds my banner unfurl.
From cape to cape, with a bridge-like shape,
    Over a torrent sea,
Sunbeam-proof, I hang like a roof,—
    The mountains its columns be.
The triumphal arch through which I march
    With hurricane, fire, and snow,
When the Powers of the air are chained to my chair,
    Is the million-coloured bow;
The sphere-fire above its soft colours wove,
    While the moist Earth was laughing below.

I am the daughter of Earth and Water,
  And the nursling of the Sky;
I pass through the pores of the ocean and shores;
  I change, but I cannot die.
For after the rain, when with never a stain,
  The pavilion of heaven is bare,
And the winds and sunbeams with their convex gleams
  Build up the blue dome of air,
I silently laugh at my own cenotaph,
  And out of the caverns of rain,
Like a child from the womb, like a ghost from the tomb,
  I arise and unbuild it again.

34   TO A SKYLARK

P. B. Shelley

Hail to thee, blithe Spirit!
  Bird thou never wert,
That from heaven, or near it,
  Pourest thy full heart
In profuse strains of unpremeditated art.

Higher still and higher
  From the earth thou springest
Like a cloud of fire;
  The blue deep thou wingest,
And singing still dost soar, and soaring ever singest.

In the golden light'ning
  Of the sunken sun,
O'er which clouds are bright'ning,
  Thou dost float and run;
Like an unbodied joy whose race is just begun.

The pale purple even
Melts around thy flight;
Like a star of heaven,
In the broad daylight
Thou art unseen, but yet I hear thy shrill delight.

Keen as are the arrows
Of that silver sphere,
Whose intense lamp narrows
In the white dawn clear
Until we hardly see—we feel that it is there.

All the earth and air
With thy voice is loud,
As, when night is bare,
From one lonely cloud
The moon rains out her beams, and heaven is overflow'd.

What thou art we know not;
What is most like thee?
From rainbow clouds there flow not
Drops so bright to see
As from thy presence showers a rain of melody.

Like a poet hidden
In the light of thought,
Singing hymns unbidden,
Till the world is wrought
To sympathy with hopes and fears it heeded not:

Like a high-born maiden
In a palace tower,
Soothing her love-laden
Soul in secret hour
With music sweet as love, which overflows her bower:

Like a glow-worm golden
In a dell of dew,
Scattering unbeholden
Its aereal hue
Among the flowers and grass, which screen it from the view!

Like a rose embower'd
In its own green leaves,
By warm winds deflower'd,
Till the scent it gives
Makes faint with too much sweet these heavy-winged thieves:

Sound of vernal showers
On the twinkling grass,
Rain-awaken'd flowers,
All that ever was
Joyous, and clear, and fresh, thy music doth surpass:

Teach us, sprite or bird,
What sweet thoughts are thine:
I have never heard
Praise of love or wine
That panted forth a flood of rapture so divine.

Chorus hymeneal,
Or triumphal chant,
Match'd with thine would be all
But an empty vaunt,
A thing wherein we feel there is some hidden want.

What objects are the fountains
Of thy happy strain?
What fields, or waves, or mountains?
What shapes of sky or plain?
What love of thine own kind? What ignorance of pain?

With thy clear keen joyance
Languor cannot be:
Shadow of annoyance
Never came near thee:
Thou lovest—but ne'er knew love's sad satiety.

Waking or asleep
Thou of death must deem
Things more true and deep
Than we mortals dream,
Or how could thy notes flow in such a crystal stream?

We look before and after,
    And pine for what is not:
Our sincerest laughter
    With some pain is fraught;
Our sweetest songs are those that tell of saddest thought.

Yet if we could scorn
    Hate, and pride, and fear;
If we were things born
    Not to shed a tear,
I know not how thy joy we ever should come near.

Better than all measures
    Of delightful sound,
Better than all treasures
    That in books are found,
Thy skill to poet were, thou scorner of the ground!

Teach me half the gladness
    That thy brain must know,
Such harmonious madness
    From my lips would flow,
The world should listen then—as I am listening now.

35   THE BURIAL OF SIR JOHN MOORE

Charles Wolfe
(1791-1823)

Not a drum was heard, not a funeral note,
    As his corse to the rampart we hurried;
Not a soldier discharged his farewell shot
    O'er the grave where our hero we buried.

We buried him darkly at dead of night,
    The sods with our bayonets turning—
By the struggling moonbeam's misty light
    And the lanthorn dimly burning.

No useless coffin enclosed his breast,
    Not in sheet nor in shroud we wound him;
But he lay like a warrior taking his rest,
    With his martial cloak around him.

Few and short were the prayers we said,
    And we spoke not a word of sorrow;
But we steadfastly gazed on the face that was dead,
    And we bitterly thought of the morrow.

We thought, as we hollow'd his narrow bed
    And smooth'd down his lonely pillow,
That the foe and the stranger would tread o'er his head,
    And we far away on the billow!

Lightly they'll talk of the spirit that's gone
    And o'er his cold ashes upbraid him—
But little he'll reck, if they let him sleep on
    In the grave where a Briton has laid him.

But half of our heavy task was done
    When the clock struck the hour for retiring;
And we heard the distant and random gun
    That the foe was sullenly firing.

Slowly and sadly we laid him down,
    From the field of his fame fresh and gory;
We carved not a line, and we raised not a stone,
    But we left him alone with his glory.

36   THE DESTRUCTION OF SENNACHERIB

Lord Byron
(1788-1824)

The Assyrian came down like the wolf on the fold,
And his cohorts were gleaming in purple and gold;
And the sheen of their spears was like stars on the sea,
When the blue wave rolls nightly on deep Galilee.

Like the leaves of the forest when summer is green,
That host with their banners at sunset were seen;
Like the leaves of the forest when autumn hath blown,
That host on the morrow lay withered and strown.

For the Angel of Death spread his wings on the blast,
And breathed on the face of the foe as he passed;
And the eyes of the sleepers waxed deadly and chill,
And their hearts but once heaved, and for ever grew still!

And there lay the steed with his nostril all wide,
But through it there rolled not the breath of his pride;
And the foam of his gasping lay white on the turf,
And cold as the spray of the rock-beating surf.

And there lay the rider distorted and pale,
With the dew on his brow, and the rust on his mail;
And the tents were all silent, the banners alone,
The lances unlifted, the trumpet unblown.

And the widows of Ashur are loud in their wail,
And the idols are broke in the temple of Baal;
And the might of the Gentile, unsmote by the sword,
Hath melted like snow in the glance of the Lord!

37   SO, WE'LL GO NO MORE
A-ROVING

Lord Byron

So, we'll go no more a-roving
    So late into the night,
Though the heart be still as loving,
    And the moon be still as bright.

For the sword outwears its sheath,
    And the soul wears out the breast,
And the heart must pause to breathe,
    And love itself have rest.

Though the night was made for loving,
 And the day returns too soon,
Yet we'll go no more a-roving
 By the light of the moon.

38   SHE WALKS IN BEAUTY

Lord Byron

She walks in beauty, like the night
 Of cloudless climes and starry skies;
And all that's best of dark and bright
 Meet in her aspect and her eyes:
Thus mellow'd to that tender light
 Which heaven to gaudy day denies.

One shade the more, one ray the less,
 Had half impair'd the nameless grace
Which waves in every raven tress,
 Or softly lightens o'er her face;
Where thoughts serenely sweet express
 How pure, how dear their dwelling-place.

And on that cheek, and o'er that brow,
 So soft, so calm, yet eloquent,
The smiles that win, the tints that glow,
 But tell of days in goodness spent,
A mind at peace with all below,
 A heart whose love is innocent!

39　　THE LAMB

William Blake
(1757-1827)

Little Lamb, who made thee?
Dost thou know who made thee?
Gave thee life, and bid thee feed
By the stream and o'er the mead;
Gave thee clothing of delight,
Softest clothing, woolly, bright;
Gave thee such a tender voice,
Making all the vales rejoice?
Little Lamb, who made thee?
Dost thou know who made thee?

Little Lamb, I'll tell thee,
Little Lamb, I'll tell thee,
He is callèd by thy name,
For He calls Himself a Lamb.
He is meek, and He is mild;
He became a little child.
I a child, and thou a lamb,
We are callèd by His name.
Little Lamb, God bless thee!
Little Lamb, God bless thee!

40　　THE TYGER

William Blake

Tyger! Tyger! burning bright
In the forests of the night,
What immortal hand or eye
Could frame thy fearful symmetry?

In what distant deeps or skies
Burnt the fire of thine eyes?
On what wings dare he aspire?
What the hand dare seize the fire?

What the shoulder, and what art,
Could twist the sinews of thy heart?
And when thy heart began to beat,
What dread hand? And what dread feet?

What the hammer? What the chain?
In what furnace was thy brain?
What the anvil? What dread grasp
Dare its deadly terrors clasp?

When the stars threw down their spears,
And water'd heaven with their tears,
Did He smile His work to see?
Did He who made the Lamb make thee?

Tyger! Tyger! burning bright
In the forests of the night,
What immortal hand or eye,
Dare frame thy fearful symmetry?

41   JERUSALEM

William Blake

And did those feet in ancient time
    Walk upon England's mountains green?
And was the holy Lamb of God
    On England's pleasant pastures seen?

And did the Countenance Divine
    Shine forth upon our clouded hills?
And was Jerusalem builded here
    Among these dark Satanic Mills?

Bring me my bow of burning gold!
    Bring me my arrows of desire!
Bring me my spear! O clouds, unfold!
    Bring me my chariot of fire!

I will not cease from mental fight,
    Nor shall my sword sleep in my hand,
Till we have built Jerusalem
    In England's green and pleasant land.

42   YOUNG LOCHINVAR

Sir Walter Scott
(1771-1832)

O, Young Lochinvar is come out of the west,
Through all the wide Border his steed was the best,
And save his good broadsword he weapons had none;
He rode all unarmed, and he rode all alone.
So faithful in love, and so dauntless in war,
There never was knight like the young Lochinvar.

He stayed not for brake, and he stopped not for stone,
He swam the Eske river where ford there was none;
But, ere he alighted at Netherby gate,
The bride had consented, the gallant came late:
For a laggard in love, and a dastard in war,
Was to wed the fair Ellen of brave Lochinvar.

So boldly he entered the Netherby Hall,
Among bride's-men and kinsmen, and brothers and all:
Then spake the bride's father, his hand on his sword
(For the poor craven bridegroom said never a word),
'O come ye in peace here, or come ye in war,
Or to dance at our bridal, young Lord Lochinvar?'

'I long wooed your daughter, my suit you denied;—
Love swells like the Solway, but ebbs like its tide—
And now I am come, with this lost love of mine
To lead but one measure, drink one cup of wine.
There are maidens in Scotland more lovely by far,
That would gladly be bride to the young Lochinvar.'

The bride kissed the goblet; the knight took it up,
He quaffed off the wine, and he threw down the cup,
She looked down to blush, and she looked up to sigh,
With a smile on her lips and a tear in her eye.
He took her soft hand, ere her mother could bar,—
'Now tread we a measure!' said young Lochinvar.

So stately his form, and so lovely her face,
That never a hall such a galliard did grace;
While her mother did fret, and her father did fume,
And the bridegroom stood dangling his bonnet and plume;
And the brid-maidens whispered, "Twere better by far
To have matched our fair cousin with young Lochinvar.'

One touch to her hand, and one word in her ear,
When they reached the hall-door, and the charger stood near;
So light to the croupe the fair lady he swung,
So light to the saddle before her he sprung!
'She is won! we are gone, over bank, bush, and scaur;
They'll have fleet steeds that follow,' quoth young Lochinvar.

There was mounting 'mong Graemes of the Netherby clan;
Forsters, Fenwicks, and Musgraves, they rode and they ran;
There was racing, and chasing, on Cannobie Lee,
But the lost bride of Netherby ne'er did they see.
So daring in love, and so dauntless in war,
Have ye e'er heard of gallant like young Lochinvar?

43   PIBROCH OF DONUIL DHU

Sir Walter Scott

Pibroch of Donuil Dhu,
  Pibroch of Donuil,
Wake thy wild voice anew,
  Summon Clan Conuil.
Come away, come away,
  Hark to the summons!
Come in your war-array,
  Gentles and commons.

Come from deep glen, and
　　From mountain so rocky,—
The war-pipe and pennon
　　Are at Inverlochy.
Come every hill-plaid, and
　　True heart that wears one,
Come every steel blade, and
　　Strong hand that bears one.

Leave untended the herd,
　　The flock without shelter;
Leave the corpse uninterr'd,
　　The bride at the altar;
Leave the deer, leave the steer,
　　Leave nets and barges:
Come with your fighting gear,
　　Broadswords and targes.

Come as the winds come, when
　　Forests are rended;
Come as the waves come, when
　　Navies are stranded:
Faster come, faster come,
　　Faster and faster,
Chief, vassal, page and groom,
　　Tenant and master.

Fast they come, fast they come;
　　See how they gather!
Wide waves the eagle plume,
　　Blended with heather.
Cast your plaids, draw your blades,
　　Forward, each man, set!
Pibroch of Donuil Dhu,
　　Knell for the onset!

44   JOCK OF HAZELDEAN

Sir Walter Scott

'Why weep ye by the tide, ladie?
    Why weep ye by the tide?
I'll wed ye to my youngest son,
    And ye shall be his bride:
And ye shall be his bride, ladie,
    Sae comely to be seen'—
But aye she loot the tears down fa'
    For Jock of Hazeldean.

'Now let this wilfu' grief be done,
    And dry that cheek so pale;
Young Frank is chief of Errington,
    And lord of Langley-dale;
His step is first in peaceful ha',
    His sword in battle keen'—
But aye she loot the tears down fa'
    For Jock of Hazeldean.

'A chain of gold ye shall not lack,
    Nor braid to bind your hair;
Nor mettled hound, nor managed hawk,
    Nor palfrey fresh and fair;
And you, the foremost of them a',
    Shall ride our forest queen'—
But aye she loot the tears down fa'
    For Jock of Hazeldean.

The kirk was deck'd at morning-tide,
    The tapers glimmer'd fair;
The priest and bridegroom wait the bride,
    And dame and knight are there.
They sought her baith by bower and ha';
    The ladie was not seen!
She's o'er the Border, and awa'
    Wi' Jock of Hazeldean.

45   KUBLA KHAN

Samuel Taylor Coleridge
(1772-1834)

In Xanadu did Kubla Khan
A stately pleasure-dome decree:
Where Alph, the sacred river, ran
Through caverns measureless to man
   Down to a sunless sea.
So twice five miles of fertile ground
With walls and towers were girdled round:
And here were gardens bright with sinuous rills,
Where blossomed many an incense-bearing tree;
And here were forests ancient as the hills,
Enfolding sunny spots of greenery.

But oh! that deep romantic chasm which slanted
Down the green hill athwart a cedarn cover!
A savage place! as holy and enchanted
As e'er beneath a waning moon was haunted
By woman wailing for her demon-lover!
And from this chasm, with ceaseless turmoil seething,
As if this earth in fast thick pants were breathing,
A mighty fountain momently was forced,
Amid whose swift half-intermitted burst
Huge fragments vaulted like rebounding hail,
Or chaffy grain beneath the thresher's flail:
And 'mid these dancing rocks at once and ever
It flung up momently the sacred river.
Five miles meandering with a mazy motion
Through wood and dale the sacred river ran,
Then reached the caverns measureless to man,
And sank in tumult to a lifeless ocean:
And 'mid this tumult Kubla heard from far
Ancestral voices prophesying war!
   The shadow of the dome of pleasure
   Floated midway on the waves;
Where was heard the mingled measure
From the fountain and the caves.
It was a miracle of rare device,
A sunny pleasure-dome with caves of ice!

A damsel with a dulcimer
In a vision once I saw:
It was an Abyssinian maid,
And on her dulcimer she played,
Singing of Mount Abora.
Could I revive within me
Her symphony and song,
To such a deep delight 'twould win me,
That with music loud and long,
I would build that dome in air,
That sunny dome! those caves of ice!
And all who heard should see them there,
And all should cry, 'Beware! Beware!
His flashing eyes, his floating hair!
Weave a circle round him thrice,
And close your eyes with holy dread,
For he on honey-dew hath fed,
And drunk the milk of Paradise.'

46   A SEA SONG

Allan Cunningham
(1784-1842)

A wet sheet and a flowing sea,
    A wind that follows fast
And fills the white and rustling sail
    And bends the gallant mast;
And bends the gallant mast, my boys,
    While like the eagle free
Away the good ship flies, and leaves
    Old England on the lee.

O for a soft and gentle wind!
    I heard a fair one cry;
But give to me the snorting breeze
    And white waves heaving high;
And white waves heaving high, my lads,
    A good ship tight and free—
The world of waters is our home,
    And merry men are we.

There's tempest in yon hornèd moon,
    And lightning in yon cloud;
But hark the music, mariners!
    The wind is piping loud;
The wind is piping loud, my boys,
    The lightning flashes free—
While the hollow oak our palace is,
    Our heritage the sea.

47   THE INCHCAPE ROCK

Robert Southey
(1774-1843)

1. THE INCHCAPE BELL.

No stir in the air, no stir in the sea,
The ship was still as she could be,
Her sails from heaven received no motion,
Her keel was steady in the ocean.

Without either sign or sound of their shock
The waves flowed over the Inchcape Rock;
So little they rose, so little they fell,
They did not move the Inchcape Bell.

The Abbot of Aberbrothok
Had placed that bell on the Inchcape Rock;
On a buoy in the storm it floated and swung,
And over the waves its warning rung.

When the Rock was hid by the surge's swell,
The mariners heard the warning bell;
And then they knew the perilous rock
And blest the Abbot of Aberbrothok.

2. SIR RALPH THE ROVER'S WICKED DEED.

The sun in heaven was shining gay,
All things were joyful on that day;
The sea-birds screamed as they wheeled around,
And there was joyaunce in their sound.

The buoy of the Inchcape Bell was seen
A darker speck on the ocean green;
Sir Ralph the Rover walked his deck,
And he fixed his eye on the darker speck.

He felt the cheering power of spring;
It made him whistle, it made him sing;
His heart was mirthful to excess,
But the Rover's mirth was wickedness.

His eye was on the Inchcape float;
Quoth he, 'My men, put out the boat,
And row me to the Inchcape Rock,
And I'll plague the Abbot of Aberbrothok.'

The boat is lowered, the boatmen row,
And to the Inchcape Rock they go;
Sir Ralph bent over from the boat,
And he cut the Bell from the Inchcape float.

Down sunk the Bell with a gurgling sound,
The bubbles rose and burst around;
Quoth Sir Ralph, 'The next who comes to the Rock
Won't bless the Abbot of Aberbrothok.'

3. SIR RALPH THE ROVER'S RETURN.

Sir Ralph the Rover sailed away,
He scoured the seas for many a day;
And now grown rich with plundered store,
He steers his course for Scotland's shore.

So thick a haze o'erspreads the sky
They cannot see the sun on high;
The wind hath blown a gale all day,
At evening it hath died away.

On the deck the Rover takes his stand,
So dark it is they see no land.
Quoth Sir Ralph, 'It will be lighter soon,
For there is the dawn of the rising Moon.'

'Canst hear,' said one, 'the breakers roar?
For methinks we should be near the shore.'
'Now where we are I cannot tell,
But I wish I could hear the Inchcape Bell.'

They hear no sound, the swell is strong;
Though the wind hath fallen, they drift along,
Till the vessel strikes with a shivering shock,—
'O Christ! it is the Inchcape Rock!'

Sir Ralph the Rover tore his hair;
He cursed himself in his despair;
The waves rush in on every side,
The ship is sinking beneath the tide.

But even in his dying fear
One dreadful sound could the Rover hear,
A sound as if with the Inchcape Bell
The Devil below was ringing his knell.

48   AFTER BLENHEIM

Robert Southey

It was a summer evening,
    Old Kaspar's work was done,
And he before his cottage door
    Was sitting in the sun:
And by him sported on the green
His little grandchild Wilhelmine.

She saw her brother Peterkin
    Roll something large and round
Which he beside the rivulet
    In playing there had found:
He came to ask what he had found
That was so large, and smooth, and round.

Old Kaspar took it from the boy
    Who stood expectant by;
And then the old man shook his head,
    And with a natural sigh
' 'Tis some poor fellow's skull,' said he,
'Who fell in the great victory.

'I find them in the garden,
    For there's many here about;
And often when I go to plough
    The ploughshare turns them out.
For many thousand men,' said he,
'Were slain in that great victory.'

'Now tell us what 'twas all about,'
    Young Peterkin, he cries;
And little Wilhelmine looks up
    With wonder-waiting eyes;
'Now tell us all about the war,
And what they fought each other for.'

'It was the English,' Kaspar cried,
    'Who put the French to rout;
But what they fought each other for
    I could not well make out.
But everybody said,' quoth he,
'That 'twas a famous victory.

'My father lived at Blenheim then,
    Yon little stream hard by;
They burnt his dwelling to the ground,
    And he was forced to fly:
So with his wife and child he fled
Nor had he where to rest his head.

'With fire and sword the country round
    Was wasted far and wide,
And many a childing mother then,
    And newborn baby died:
But things like that, you know, must be
At every famous victory.

'They say it was a shocking sight
    After the field was won;
For many thousand bodies here
    Lay rotting in the sun:
But things like that, you know, must be
After a famous victory.

'Great praise the Duke of Marlboro' won
    And our good Prince Eugene.'
'Why 'twas a very wicked thing!'
    Said little Wilhelmine;
'Nay . . . nay . . . my little girl,' quoth he,
'It was a famous victory.

'And everybody praised the Duke
    Who this great fight did win.'
'But what good came of it at last?'
    Quoth little Peterkin.
'Why that I cannot tell,' said he,
'But 'twas a famous victory.'

49   **BISHOP HATTO**

Robert Southey

The summer and autumn had been so wet,
That in winter the corn was growing yet,
'Twas a piteous sight to see all around
The grain lie rotting on the ground.

Every day the starving poor
Crowded around Bishop Hatto's door,
For he had a plentiful last-year's store,
And all the neighbourhood could tell
His granaries were furnished well.

At last Bishop Hatto appointed a day
To quiet the poor without delay;
He bade them to his great barn repair,
And they should have food for the winter there.

Rejoiced such tidings good to hear,
The poor folk flocked from far and near;
The great barn was full as it could hold
Of women and children, and young and old.

Then when he saw it could hold no more,
Bishop Hatto he made fast the door;
And while for mercy on Christ they call,
He set fire to the barn and burnt them all.

'I' faith, 'tis an excellent bonfire!' quoth he,
'And the country is greatly obliged to me,
For ridding it in these times forlorn
Of rats that only consume the corn.'

So then to his palace returned he,
And he sat down to supper merrily,
And he slept that night like an innocent man;
But Bishop Hatto never slept again.

In the morning as he entered the hall
Where his picture hung against the wall,
A sweat like death all over him came,
For the rats had eaten it out of the frame.

As he looked there came a man from his farm,
He had a countenance white with alarm;
'My Lord, I opened your granaries this morn,
And the rats had eaten all your corn.'

Another came running presently,
And he was pale as pale could be,
'Fly! my Lord Bishop, fly!' quoth he,
'Ten thousand rats are coming this way—
The Lord forgive you for yesterday!'

'I'll go to my tower on the Rhine,' replied he,
' 'Tis the safest place in Germany;
The walls are high and the shores are steep,
And the stream is strong and the water deep.'

Bishop Hatto fearfully hastened away,
And he crossed the Rhine without delay,
And reached his tower, and barred with care
All windows, doors, and loop-holes there.

He laid him down and closed his eyes;—
But soon a scream made him arise,
He stared and saw two eyes of flame
On his pillow from whence the screaming came.

He listened and looked—it was only the cat;
But the Bishop he grew more fearful for that,
For she sat screaming, mad with fear
At the army of rats that were drawing near.

For they have swum over the river so deep,
And they have climbed the shores so steep,
And up the tower their way is bent,
To do the work for which they were sent.

They are not to be told by the dozen or score,
By thousands they come, and by myriads and more,
Such numbers had never been heard of before,
Such a judgment had never been witnessed of yore.

Down on his knees the Bishop fell
And faster and faster his beads did he tell,
As louder and louder drawing near
The gnawing of their teeth he could hear.

And in at the window and in at the door,
And through the walls helter-skelter they pour,
And down from the ceiling, and up through the floor,
From the right and the left, from behind and before,
From within and without, from above and below,
And all at once to the Bishop they go.

They have whetted their teeth against the stones,
And now they pick the Bishop's bones;
They gnawed the flesh from every limb,
For they were sent to do judgment on him!

50   HOHENLINDEN

Thomas Campbell
(1777-1844)

On Linden, when the sun was low,
All bloodless lay the untrodden snow,
And dark as winter was the flow
   Of Iser, rolling rapidly.

But Linden saw another sight,
When the drum beat at dead of night,
Commanding fires of death to light
   The darkness of her scenery.

By torch and trumpet fast array'd,
Each horseman drew his battle-blade,
And furious every charger neigh'd
   To join the dreadful revelry.

Then shook the hills with thunder riven;
Then rush'd the steed, to battle driven;
And louder than the bolts of heaven
   Far flash'd the red artillery.

But redder yet that light shall glow
On Linden's hills of stained snow;
And bloodier yet the torrent flow
    Of Iser, rolling rapidly.

'Tis morn, but scarce yon level sun
Can pierce the war-clouds, rolling dun,
Where furious Frank and fiery Hun
    Shout in their sulphurous canopy.

The combat deepens.   On, ye brave,
Who rush to glory, or the grave!
Wave, Munich! all thy banners wave,
    And charge with all thy chivalry!

Few, few shall part where many meet!
The snow shall be their winding-sheet,
And every turf beneath their feet
    Shall be a soldier's sepulchre.

51   YE MARINERS OF ENGLAND

Thomas Campbell

Ye Mariners of England
That guard our native seas,
Whose flag has braved a thousand years,
The battle and the breeze—
Your glorious standard launch again
To match another foe!
And sweep through the deep,
While the stormy winds do blow,—
While the battle rages loud and long
And the stormy winds do blow.

The spirits of your fathers
Shall start from every wave!
For the deck it was their field of fame,
And Ocean was their grave.
Where Blake and mighty Nelson fell
Your manly hearts shall glow,
As ye sweep through the deep,
While the stormy winds do blow,—
While the battle rages loud and long
And the stormy winds do blow.

Britannia needs no bulwarks,
No towers along the steep;
Her march is o'er the mountain-waves,
Her home is on the deep.
With thunders from her native oak
She quells the floods below,
As they roar on the shore,
When the stormy winds do blow,—
When the battle rages loud and long,
And the stormy winds do blow.

The meteor flag of England
Shall yet terrific burn;
Till danger's troubled night depart
And the star of peace return.
Then, then, ye ocean-warriors!
Our song and feast shall flow
To the fame of your name,
When the storm has ceased to blow,—
When the fiery fight is heard no more,
And the storm has ceased to blow.

THE SONG OF THE SHIRT

Thomas Hood
(*1799-1845*)

With fingers weary and worn,
    With eyelids heavy and red,
A woman sat, in unwomanly rags,
    Plying her needle and thread—
        Stitch! stitch! stitch!
    In poverty, hunger, and dirt,
And still with a voice of dolorous pitch
    She sang the 'Song of the shirt.'

    'Work! work! work!
While the cock is crowing aloof!
    And work—work—work,
Till the stars shine through the roof!
    It's Oh! to be a slave
        Along with the barbarous Turk,
Where woman has never a soul to save,
    If this is Christian work!

    'Work—work—work
Till the brain begins to swim:
    Work—work—work
Till the eyes are heavy and dim!
Seam, and gusset, and band,
    Band, and gusset, and seam,
Till over the buttons I fall asleep,
    And sew them on in a dream!

'Oh, Men with Sisters dear!
    Oh, Men with Mothers and Wives!
It is not linen you're wearing out,
    But human creatures' lives!
        Stitch—stitch—stitch,
    In poverty, hunger, and dirt,
Sewing at once, with a double thread,
    A Shroud as well as a Shirt.

'But why do I talk of Death?
That Phantom of grisly bone,
I hardly fear his terrible shape,
    It seems so like my own—
    It seems so like my own,
    Because of the fasts I keep;
O God! that bread should be so dear,
    And flesh and blood so cheap!

'Work—work—work!
    My labour never flags;
And what are its wages?   A bed of straw,
    A crust of bread—and rags.
That shatter'd roof,—and this naked floor—
    A table—a broken chair—
And a wall so blank, my shadow I thank
    For sometimes falling there!

'Work—work—work!
From weary chime to chime,
    Work—work—work—
As prisoners work for crime!
    Band, and gusset, and seam,
    Seam, and gusset, and band,
Till the heart is sick, and the brain benumb'd,
    As well as the weary hand.

'Work—work—work,
In the dull December light,
    And work—work—work,
When the weather is warm and bright—
While underneath the eaves
    The brooding swallows cling,
As if to show me their sunny backs
    And twit me with the spring.

- 'Oh! but to breathe the breath
Of the cowslip and primrose sweet!—
    With the sky above my head,
And the grass beneath my feet;
For only one short hour
    To feel as I used to feel,
Before I knew the woes of want
    And the walk that costs a meal!

'Oh! but for one short hour!
    A respite however brief!
No blessed leisure for Love or Hope,
    But only time for Grief!
A little weeping would ease my heart,
    But in their briny bed
My tears must stop, for every drop
    Hinders needle and thread!

    'Seam, and gusset, and band,
Band, and gusset, and seam,
    Work, work, work,
Like the Engine that works by Steam!
A mere machine of iron and wood
    That toils for Mammon's sake—
Without a brain to ponder and craze
    Or a heart to feel—and break!'

With fingers weary and worn,
    With eyelids heavy and red,
A woman sat, in unwomanly rags,
    Plying her needle and thread—
        Stitch! stitch! stitch!
    In poverty, hunger, and dirt,
And still with a voice of dolorous pitch,—
Would that its tone could reach the Rich!—
    She sang this 'Song of the Shirt.'

53   I REMEMBER, I REMEMBER

Thomas Hood

I remember, I remember,
The house where I was born,
The little window where the sun
Came peeping in at morn;
He never came a wink too soon,
Nor brought too long a day;
But now, I often wish the night
Had borne my breath away!

I remember, I remember,
The roses, red and white,
The violets, and the lily-cups—
Those flowers made of light!
The lilacs where the robin built,
And where my brother set
The laburnum on his birthday,—
The tree is living yet!

I remember, I remember,
Where I was used to swing,
And thought the air must rush as fresh
To swallows on the wing;
My spirit flew in feathers then
That is so heavy now,
And summer pools could hardly cool
The fever on my brow.

I remember, I remember,
The fir-trees dark and high;
I used to think their slender tops
Were close against the sky:
It was a childish ignorance,
But now 'tis little joy
To know I'm farther off from heaven
Than when I was a boy.

54   REMEMBRANCE

Emily Brontë
(1818-1848)

Cold in the earth—and the deep snow piled above thee,
    Far, far removed, cold in the dreary grave!
Have I forgot, my only Love, to love thee,
    Severed at last by Time's all-severing wave?

Now, when alone, do my thoughts no longer hover
    Over the mountains, on that northern shore,
Resting their wings where heath and fern-leaves cover
    Thy noble heart for ever, ever more?

Cold in the earth—and fifteen wild Decembers
    From those brown hills have melted into spring:
Faithful, indeed, is the spirit that remembers
    After such years of change and suffering!

Sweet Love of youth, forgive, if I forget thee,
    While the world's tide is bearing me along;
Other desires and other hopes beset me,
    Hopes which obscure, but cannot do thee wrong!

No later light has lightened up my heaven,
    No second morn has ever shone for me;
All my life's bliss from thy dear life was given,
    All my life's bliss is in the grave with thee.

But, when the days of golden dreams had perished,
    And even Despair was powerless to destroy;
Then did I learn how existence could be cherished,
    Strengthened, and fed without the aid of joy.

Then did I check the tears of useless passion—
    Weaned my young soul from yearning after thine;
Sternly denied its burning wish to hasten
    Down to that tomb already more than mine.

And, even yet, I dare not let it languish,
    Dare not indulge in memory's rapturous pain;
Once drinking deep of that divinest anguish,
    How could I seek the empty world again?

55 COMPOSED UPON WESTMINSTER BRIDGE, SEPT. 3, 1802

William Wordsworth
(1770-1850)

Earth has not anything to show more fair:
Dull would he be of soul who could pass by
A sight so touching in its majesty:
This City now doth, like a garment, wear
The beauty of the morning; silent, bare,
Ships, towers, domes, theatres, and temples lie
Open unto the fields, and to the sky;
All bright and glittering in the smokeless air.
Never did sun more beautifully steep
In his first splendour, valley, rock, or hill;
Ne'er saw I, never felt, a calm so deep!
The river glideth at his own sweet will:
Dear God! the very houses seem asleep;
And all that mighty heart is lying still!

56 THE SOLITARY REAPER

William Wordsworth

Behold her, single in the field,
Yon solitary Highland Lass!
Reaping and singing by herself;
Stop here, or gently pass!
Alone she cuts and binds the grain,
And sings a melancholy strain;
O listen! for the vale profound
Is overflowing with the sound.

No nightingale did ever chaunt
More welcome notes to weary bands
Of travellers in some shady haunt,
Among Arabian sands:
A voice so thrilling ne'er was heard
In spring-time from the cuckoo-bird,
Breaking the silence of the seas
Among the farthest Hebrides.

Will no one tell me what she sings?
Perhaps the plaintive numbers flow
For old, unhappy, far-off things,
And battles long ago:
Or is it some more humble lay,
Familiar matter of to-day?
Some natural sorrow, loss, or pain,
That has been, and may be again?

Whate'er the theme, the maiden sang
As if her song could have no ending;
I saw her singing at her work,
And o'er the sickle bending;
I listen'd, motionless and still;
And, as I mounted up the hill,
The music in my heart I bore,
Long after it was heard no more.

57   THE DAFFODILS

William Wordsworth

I wander'd lonely as a cloud
That floats on high o'er vales and hills,
When all at once I saw a crowd,
A host, of golden daffodils;
Beside the lake, beneath the trees,
Fluttering and dancing in the breeze.

Continuous as the stars that shine
And twinkle on the Milky Way,
They stretch'd in never-ending line
Along the margin of a bay:
Ten thousand saw I at a glance
Tossing their heads in sprightly dance.

The waves beside them danced, but they
Out-did the sparkling waves in glee:
A poet could not but be gay
In such a jocund company:
I gazed—and gazed—but little thought
What wealth the show to me had brought:

For oft, when on my couch I lie
In vacant or in pensive mood,
They flash upon that inward eye
Which is the bliss of solitude;
And then my heart with pleasure fills,
And dances with the daffodils.

58   TO THE CUCKOO

William Wordsworth

O blithe new-comer! I have heard,
I hear thee and rejoice:
O Cuckoo! shall I call thee Bird,
Or but a wandering Voice?

While I am lying on the grass
Thy twofold shout I hear,—
From hill to hill it seems to pass,
At once far off and near.

Though babbling only to the vale,
Of sunshine and of flowers,
Thou bringest unto me a tale
Of visionary hours.

Thrice welcome, darling of the Spring!
Even yet thou art to me
No bird, but an invisible thing,
A voice, a mystery;

The same whom in my school-boy days
I listened to; that cry
Which made me look a thousand ways
In bush, and tree, and sky.

To seek thee did I often rove
Through woods and on the green;
And thou wert still a hope, a love;
Still longed for, never seen.

And I can listen to thee yet;
Can lie upon the plain
And listen, till I do beget
That golden time again.

O blessèd Bird! the earth we pace
Again appears to be
An unsubstantial, faery place;
That is fit home for Thee!

59   ABOU BEN ADHEM

Leigh Hunt
(1784-1859)

Abou Ben Adhem (may his tribe increase!)
Awoke one night from a deep dream of peace,
And saw, within the moonlight in his room,
Making it rich, and like a lily in bloom,
An angel writing in a book of gold:—
Exceeding peace had made Ben Adhem bold,
And to the presence in the room he said,
'What writest thou?'—The vision raised its head,
And with a look made of all sweet accord,
Answered, 'The names of those who love the Lord.'
'And is mine one?' said Abou. 'Nay, not so,'
Replied the angel. Abou spoke more low,
But cheerly still; and said, 'I pray thee, then,
Write me as one that loves his fellow-men.'

The angel wrote, and vanished.   The next night
It came again with a great wakening light,
And showed the names whom love of God had blessed,
And lo! Ben Adhem's name led all the rest.

60   HOW DO I LOVE THEE?

Elizabeth Barrett Browning
(1806-1861)

How do I love thee?   Let me count the ways.
I love thee to the depth and breadth and height
My soul can reach, when feeling out of sight
For the ends of Being and ideal Grace.
I love thee to the level of every day's
Most quiet need, by sun and candlelight.
I love thee freely, as men strive for Right;
I love thee purely, as they turn from Praise;
I love thee with the passion put to use
In my old griefs, and with my childhood's faith.
I love thee with a love I seemed to lose
With my lost saints,—I love thee with the breath,
Smiles, tears, of all my life!—and, if God choose,
I shall but love thee better after death.

61   SAY NOT THE STRUGGLE
NAUGHT AVAILETH

A. H. Clough
(1819-1861)

Say not the struggle naught availeth,
    The labour and the wounds are vain,
The enemy faints not, nor faileth,
    And as things have been they remain.

76

If hopes were dupes, fears may be liars;
  It may be, in yon smoke conceal'd,
Your comrades chase e'en now the fliers,
  And, but for you, possess the field.

For while the tired waves, vainly breaking,
  Seem here no painful inch to gain,
Far back, through creeks and inlets making,
  Comes silent, flooding in, the main.

And not by eastern windows only,
  When daylight comes, comes in the light;
In front the sun climbs slow, how slowly!
  But westward, look, the land is bright!

62   LITTLE TROTTY WAGTAIL

John Clare
(1793-1864)

Little trotty wagtail, he went in the rain,
And tittering, tottering sideways he ne'er got straight again;
He stooped to get a worm, and looked up to catch a fly,
And then he flew away ere his feathers they were dry.

Little trotty wagtail, he waddled in the mud,
And left his little footmarks, trample where he would.
And waddled in the water-pudge, and waggle went his tail,
And chirrup up his wings to dry upon the garden rail.

Little trotty wagtail, you nimble all about,
And in the dimpling water-pudge you waddle in and out;
Your home is nigh at hand, and in the warm pigsty,
So, little Master Wagtail, I'll bid you a goodbye.

63 THE WAR SONG OF DINAS VAWR

Thomas Love Peacock
(1785-1866)

The mountain sheep are sweeter,
But the valley sheep are fatter;
We therefore deemed it meeter
To carry off the latter.
We made an expedition;
We met a host and quelled it;
We forced a strong position,
And killed the men who held it.

On Dyfed's richest valley,
Where herds of kine were browsing,
We made a mighty sally,
To furnish our carousing.
Fierce warriors rushed to meet us;
We met them, and o'erthrew them:
They struggled hard to beat us;
But we conquered them, and slew them.

As we drove our prize at leisure,
The king marched forth to catch us:
His rage surpassed all measure,
But his people could not match us.
He fled to his hall-pillars;
And, ere our force we led off,
Some sacked his house and cellars,
While others cut his head off.

We there, in strife bewildering,
Spilt blood enough to swim in:
We orphaned many children,
And widowed many women.
The eagles and the ravens
We glutted with our foemen:
The heroes and the cravens,
The spearmen and the bowmen.

We brought away from battle,
And much their land bemoaned them,
Two thousand head of cattle,
And the head of him who owned them:
Ednyfed, King of Dyfed,
His head was borne before us;
His wine and beasts supplied our feasts,
And his overthrow, our chorus.

64   THE THREE MEN OF GOTHAM

Thomas Love Peacock

Seamen three!   What men be ye?
Gotham's three wise men we be.
Whither in your bowl so free?
To rake the moon from out the sea.
The bowl goes trim.   The moon doth shine.
And our ballast is old wine.
And your ballast is old wine.

Who art thou, so fast adrift?
I am he they call Old Care.
Here on board we will thee lift.
No: I may not enter there.
Wherefore so?   'Tis Jove's decree,
In a bowl Care may not be.
In a bowl Care may not be.

Fear ye not the waves that roll?
No: in charmed bowl we swim.
What the charm that floats the bowl?
Water may not pass the brim.
The bowl goes trim.   The moon doth shine.
And our ballast is old wine.
And your ballast is old wine.

65   THE KNIGHT'S LEAP

Charles Kingsley
(1819-1875)

'So the foeman has fired the gate, men of mine;
    And the water is spent and done?
Then bring me a cup of the red Ahr-wine—
    I never shall drink but this one.

'And reach me my harness, and saddle my horse,
    And lead him me round to the door:
He must take such a leap to-night perforce
    As horse never took before.

'I have lived by the saddle for years a score;
    And if I must die on tree—
The old saddle-tree which has borne me of yore
    Is the properest timber for me.

'I have lived my life, I have fought my fight,
    I have drunk my share of wine;
From Trier to Cöln there was never a knight
    Lived a merrier life than mine.

'So now to show bishop, and burgher, and priest,
    How the Altenahr hawk can die:
If they smoke the old falcon out of his nest,
    He must take to his wings and fly.'

He harnessed himself by the clear moonshine,
    And he mounted his horse at the door;
And he took such a pull of the red Ahr-wine
    As man never took before.

He spurred the old horse, and he held him tight,
    And he leapt him out over the wall;
Out over the cliff, out into the night,
    Three hundred feet of fall.

They found him next morning below in the glen,
And never a bone in him whole—
But Heaven may yet have more mercy than men
On such a bold rider's soul.

66   THE SANDS OF DEE

Charles Kingsley

'O Mary, go and call the cattle home,
And call the cattle home,
And call the cattle home,
Across the sands of Dee!'
The western wind was wild and dank with foam,
And all alone went she.

The western tide crept up along the sand,
And o'er and o'er the sand,
And round and round the sand,
As far as eye could see.
The rolling mist came down and hid the land:
And never home came she.

'Oh! is it weed, or fish, or floating hair—
A tress of golden hair,
A drowned maiden's hair,
Above the nets at sea?
Was never salmon yet that shone so fair
Among the stakes on Dee.'

They rowed her in across the rolling foam,
The cruel crawling foam,
The cruel hungry foam,
To her grave beside the sea:
But still the boatmen hear her call the cattle home
Across the sands of Dee.

67   REQUIESCAT

Matthew Arnold
(1822-1888)

Strew on her roses, roses,
    And never a spray of yew!
In quiet she reposes:
    Ah! would that I did too!

Her mirth the world required:
    She bath'd it in smiles of glee,
But her heart was tired, tired,
    And now they let her be.

Her life was turning, turning,
    In mazes of heat and sound.
But for peace her soul was yearning,
    And now peace laps her round.

Her cabin'd, ample spirit,
    It flutter'd and fail'd for breath.
To-night it doth inherit
    The vasty Hall of Death.

68   DOVER BEACH

Matthew Arnold

The sea is calm to-night.
The tide is full, the moon lies fair
Upon the straits;—on the French coast the light
Gleams and is gone; the cliffs of England stand,
Glimmering and vast, out in the tranquil bay.

Come to the window, sweet is the night-air!
Only, from the long line of spray
Where the sea meets the moon-blanch'd land,
Listen! you hear the grating roar
Of pebbles which the waves draw back, and fling,
At their return, up the high strand,
Begin, and cease, and then again begin,
With tremulous cadence slow, and bring
The eternal note of sadness in.

Sophocles long ago
Heard it on the Aegean, and it brought
Into his mind the turbid ebb and flow
Of human misery; we
Find also in the sound a thought,
Hearing it by this distant northern sea.

The Sea of Faith
Was once, too, at the full, and round earth's shore
Lay like the folds of a bright girdle furl'd.
But now I only hear
Its melancholy, long, withdrawing roar,
Retreating, to the breath
Of the night-wind, down the vast edges drear
And naked shingles of the world.

Ah, love, let us be true
To one another! for the world, which seems
To lie before us like a land of dreams,
So various, so beautiful, so new,
Hath really neither joy, nor love, nor light,
Nor certitude, nor peace, nor help for pain;
And we are here as on a darkling plain
Swept with confused alarms of struggle and flight,
Where ignorant armies clash by night.

THE JUMBLIES

Edward Lear
(*1812-1888*)

They went to sea in a Sieve, they did,
    In a Sieve they went to sea:
In spite of all their friends could say,
On a winter's morn, on a stormy day,
    In a Sieve they went to sea!
And when the Sieve turned round and round,
And everyone cried, 'You'll all be drowned!'
They called aloud, 'Our Sieve ain't big,
But we don't care a button! we don't care a fig!
    In a Sieve we'll go to sea!'
        Far and few, far and few,
        Are the lands where the Jumblies live;
        Their heads are green, and their hands are blue,
        And they went to sea in a Sieve.

They sailed away in a Sieve, they did,
    In a Sieve they sailed so fast,
With only a beautiful pea-green veil
Tied with a riband by way of a sail,
    To a small tobacco-pipe mast;
And everyone said, who saw them go,
'O won't they be soon upset, you know!
For the sky is dark, and the voyage is long,
And happen what may, it's extremely wrong
    In a Sieve to sail so fast!'
        Far and few, far and few,
        Are the lands where the Jumblies live;
        Their heads are green, and their hands are blue,
        And they went to sea in a Sieve.

The water it soon came in, it did,
   The water it soon came in;
So to keep them dry, they wrapped their feet
In a pinky paper all folded neat,
   And they fastened it down with a pin.
And they passed the night in a crockery-jar,
And each of them said, 'How wise we are!
Though the sky be dark, and the voyage be long,
Yet we never can think we were rash or wrong,
   While round in our Sieve we spin!'
      Far and few, far and few,
         Are the lands where the Jumblies live;
      Their heads are green, and their hands are blue,
         And they went to sea in a Sieve.

And all night long they sailed away;
   And when the sun went down,
They whistled and warbled a moony song
To the echoing sound of a coppery gong,
   In the shade of the mountains brown.
'O Timballo! How happy we are,
When we live in a Sieve and a crockery-jar,
And all night long in the moonlight pale,
We sail away with a pea-green sail,
   In the shade of the mountains brown!'
      Far and few, far and few,
         Are the lands where the Jumblies live;
      Their heads are green, and their hands are blue,
         And they went to sea in a Sieve.

They sailed to the Western Sea, they did,
   To a land all covered with trees,
And they bought an Owl, and a useful Cart,
And a pound of Rice, and a Cranberry Tart,
   And a hive of silvery Bees.
And they bought a Pig, and some green Jack-daws,
And a lovely Monkey with lollipop paws,
And forty bottles of Ring-Bo-Ree,
   And no end of Stilton Cheese.
      Far and few, far and few,
         Are the lands where the Jumblies live;
      Their heads are green, and their hands are blue.
         And they went to sea in a Sieve.

And in twenty years they all came back,
    In twenty years or more,
And everyone said, 'How tall they've grown!
For they've been to the Lakes, and the Torrible Zone,
    And the hills of the Chankly Bore!'
And they drank their health, and gave them a feast
Of dumplings made of beautiful yeast;
And everyone said, 'If we only live,
We too will go to sea in a Sieve,—
    To the hills of the Chankly Bore!'
        Far and few, far and few,
            Are the lands where the Jumblies live;
        Their heads are green, and their hands are blue,
            And they went to sea in a Sieve.

70   THE PELICAN CHORUS

Edward Lear

King and Queen of the Pelicans we;
No other Birds so grand we see!
None but we have feet like fins!
With lovely leathery throats and chins!
    Ploffskin, Pluffskin, Pelican jee,
    We think no Birds so happy as we!
    Plumpskin, Ploshskin, Pelican jill,
    We think so then, and we thought so still!

We live on the Nile. The Nile we love.
By night we sleep on the cliffs above;
By day we fish, and at eve we stand
On long bare islands of yellow sand.
And when the sun sinks slowly down
And the great rock walls grow dark and brown,
Where the purple river rolls fast and dim
And the Ivory Ibis starlike skim,
Wing to wing we dance around,—
Stamping our feet with a flumpy sound,—
Opening our mouths as Pelicans ought,
And this is the song we nightly snort:—
    Ploffskin, Pluffskin, Pelican jee,
    We think no Birds so happy as we!
    Plumpskin, Ploshskin, Pelican jill,
    We think so then, and we thought so still!

Last year came out our Daughter, Dell;
And all the Birds received her well.
To do her honour, a feast we made
For every bird that can swim or wade.
Herons and Gulls, and Cormorants black,
Cranes, and Flamingoes with scarlet back,
Plovers and Storks, and Geese in clouds,
Swans and Dilberry Ducks in crowds.
Thousands of Birds in wondrous flight!
They ate and drank and danced all night,
And echoing back from the rocks you heard
Multitude-echoes from Bird and Bird,—
    Ploffskin, Pluffskin, Pelican jee,
    We think no Birds so happy as we!
    Plumpskin, Ploshskin, Pelican jill,
    We think so then, and we thought so still!

Yes, they came; and among the rest,
The King of the Cranes all grandly dressed.
Such a lovely tail! Its feathers float
Between the ends of his blue dress-coat;
With pea-green trousers all so neat,
And a delicate frill to hide his feet,—
(For though no one speaks of it, every one knows,
He has got no webs between his toes!)

As soon as he saw our Daughter, Dell,
In violent love that Crane King fell,—
On seeing her waddling form so fair,
With a wreath of shrimps in her short white hair.
And before the end of the next long day,
Our Dell had given her heart away;
For the King of the Cranes had won that heart,
With a Crocodile's egg and a large fish-tart.
She vowed to marry the King of the Cranes,
Leaving the Nile for stranger plains;
And away they flew in a gathering crowd
Of endless birds in a lengthening cloud.
    Ploffskin, Pluffskin, Pelican jee,
    We think no Birds so happy as we!
    Plumpskin, Ploshskin, Pelican jill,
    We think so then, and we thought so still!

And far away in the twilight sky,
We heard them singing a lessening cry,—
Farther and farther till out of sight,
And we stood alone in the silent night!
Often since, in the nights of June,
We sit on the sand and watch the moon;—
She has gone to the great Gromboolian plain,
And we probably never shall meet again!
Oft, in the long still nights of June,
We sit on the rocks and watch the moon;—
She dwells by the streams of the Chankly Bore,
And we probably never shall see her more.
    Ploffskin, Pluffskin, Pelican jee,
    We think no Birds so happy as we!
    Plumpskin, Ploshskin, Pelican jill,
    We think so then, and we thought so still!

71 THE OWL AND THE PUSSY-CAT

Edward Lear

The Owl and the Pussy-cat went to sea
    In a beautiful pea-green boat,
They took some honey, and plenty of money,
    Wrapped up in a five-pound note.
The Owl looked up to the stars above,
    And sang to a small guitar,
'O lovely Pussy! O Pussy, my love,
    What a beautiful Pussy you arc,
        You are,
        You are!
    What a beautiful Pussy you are!'

Pussy said to the Owl, 'You elegant fowl!
    How charmingly sweet you sing!
O let us be married! too long we have tarried:
    But what shall we do for a ring?'
They sailed away, for a year and a day,
    To the land where the Bong-tree grows,
And there in a wood a Piggy-wig stood,
    With a ring at the end of his nose,
        His nose,
        His nose,
    With a ring at the end of his nose.

'Dear Pig, are you willing to sell for one shilling
    Your ring?' Said the Piggy, 'I will.'
So they took it away, and were married next day
    By the Turkey who lives on the hill.
They dined on mince, and slices of quince,
    Which they ate with a runcible spoon;
And hand in hand, on the edge of the sand,
    They danced by the light of the moon,
        The moon,
        The moon,
    They danced by the light of the moon.

72 HOME-THOUGHTS FROM ABROAD

Robert Browning
(1812-1889)

Oh, to be in England,
Now that April's there,
And whoever wakes in England
Sees, some morning, unaware,
That the lowest boughs and the brushwood sheaf
Round the elm-tree bole are in tiny leaf,
While the chaffinch sings on the orchard bough
In England—now!

And after April, when May follows,
And the whitethroat builds, and all the swallows—
Hark! where my blossomed pear-tree in the hedge
Leans to the field and scatters on the clover
Blossoms and dewdrops—at the bent spray's edge—
That's the wise thrush; he sings each song twice over,
Lest you should think he never could recapture
The first fine careless rapture!
And though the fields look rough with hoary dew,
All will be gay when noontide wakes anew
The buttercups, the little children's dower,
—Far brighter than this gaudy melon-flower!

73 HOW THEY BROUGHT THE GOOD NEWS FROM GHENT TO AIX

Robert Browning

I sprang to the stirrup, and Joris, and he;
I galloped, Dirck galloped, we galloped all three;
'Good speed!' cried the watch, as the gate-bolts undrew;
'Speed!' echoed the wall to us galloping through;
Behind shut the postern, the lights sank to rest,
And into the midnight we galloped abreast.

Not a word to each other; we kept the great pace
Neck by neck, stride by stride, never changing our place;
I turned in my saddle and made its girths tight,
Then shortened each stirrup, and set the pique right,
Rebuckled the cheek-strap, chained slacker the bit,
Nor galloped less steadily Roland a whit.

'Twas moonset at starting; but while we drew near
Lokeren, the cocks crew and twilight dawned clear;
At Boom, a great yellow star came out to see;
At Duffeld, 'twas morning as plain as could be;
And from Mecheln church-steeple we heard the half-chime,
So Joris broke silence with, 'Yet there is time!'

At Aerschot, up leaped of a sudden the sun,
And against him the cattle stood black every one,
To stare thro' the mist at us galloping past,
And I saw my stout galloper Roland at last,
With resolute shoulders, each butting away
The haze, as some bluff river headland its spray.

And his low head and crest, just one sharp ear bent back
For my voice, and the other pricked out on his track;
And one eye's black intelligence—ever that glance
O'er its white edge at me, his own master, askance!
And the thick heavy spume-flakes which aye and anon
His fierce lips shook upwards in galloping on.

By Hasselt, Dirck groaned; and, cried Joris, 'Stay spur!—
Your Roos galloped bravely, the fault's not in her,
We'll remember at Aix'—for one heard the quick wheeze
Of her chest, saw the stretched neck and staggering knees,
And sunk tail, and horrible heave of the flank,
As down on her haunches she shuddered and sank.

So we were left galloping, Joris and I,
Past Looz and past Tongres, no cloud in the sky;
The broad sun above laughed a pitiless laugh,
'Neath our feet broke the brittle bright stubble like chaff;
Till over by Dalhem a dome-spire sprang white,
And 'Gallop,' gasped Joris, 'for Aix is in sight!'

'How they'll greet us!'—and all in a moment his roan
Rolled neck and croup over, lay dead as a stone;
And there was my Roland to bear the whole weight
Of the news which alone could save Aix from her fate,
With his nostrils like pits full of blood to the brim,
And with circles of red for his eye-sockets' rim.

Then I cast loose my buffcoat, each holster let fall,
Shook off both my jack-boots, let go belt and all,
Stood up in the stirrup, leaned, patted his ear,
Called my Roland his pet-name, my horse without peer;
Clapped my hands, laughed and sang, any noise, bad or good,
Till at length into Aix Roland galloped and stood.

And all I remember is, friends flocking round
As I sat with his head 'twixt my knees on the ground;
And no voice but was praising this Roland of mine,
As I poured down his throat our last measure of wine,
Which (the burgesses voted by common consent)
Was no more than his due who brought good news from Ghent.

74 INCIDENT OF THE FRENCH
CAMP

Robert Browning

You know, we French stormed Ratisbon:
    A mile or so away,
On a little mound, Napoleon
    Stood on our storming day;
With neck out-thrust, you fancy how,
    Legs wide, arms locked behind,
As if to balance the prone brow
    Oppressive with its mind.

92

Just as perhaps he mused, 'My plans
    That soar, to earth may fall,
Let once my army-leader Lannes
    Waver at yonder wall,'—
Out 'twixt the battery-smokes there flew
    A rider, bound on bound
Full-galloping; nor bridle drew
    Until he reached the mound.

Then off there flung in smiling joy,
    And held himself erect
By just his horse's mane, a boy:
    You hardly could suspect—
(So tight he kept his lips compressed,
    Scarce any blood came through)
You looked twice ere you saw his breast
    Was all but shot in two.

'Well,' cried he, 'Emperor, by God's grace
    We've got you Ratisbon!
The Marshal's in the market-place,
    And you'll be there anon,
To see your flag-bird flap his vans
    Where I, to heart's desire,
Perched him!' The Chief's eye flashed; his plans
    Soared up again like fire.

The Chief's eye flashed; but presently
    Softened itself, as sheathes
A film the mother-eagle's eye
    When her bruised eaglet breathes:
'You're wounded!' 'Nay,' his soldier's pride
    Touched to the quick, he said:
'I'm killed, Sire!' And, his Chief beside,
    Smiling, the boy fell dead.

PROSPICE

Robert Browning

Fear death?—to feel the fog in my throat,
 The mist in my face,
When the snows begin, and the blasts denote
 I am nearing the place,
The power of the night, the press of the storm,
 The post of the foe;
Where he stands, the Arch Fear in a visible form,
 Yet the strong man must go:
For the journey is done and the summit attained,
 And the barriers fall,
Though a battle's to fight ere the guerdon be gained,
 The reward of it all.
I was ever a fighter, so—one fight more,
 The best and the last!
I would hate that death bandaged my eyes, and forbore,
 And bade me creep past.
No! let me taste the whole of it, fare like my peers
 The heroes of old,
Bear the brunt, in a minute pay glad life's arrears
 Of pain, darkness and cold.
For sudden the worst turns the best to the brave,
 The black minute's at end,
And the elements' rage, the fiend-voices that rave,
 Shall dwindle, shall blend,
Shall change, shall become first a peace out of pain,
 Then a light, then thy breast,
O thou soul of my soul! I shall clasp thee again,
 And with God be the rest!

76　　PIED BEAUTY

Gerard Manley Hopkins
(1844-1889)

Glory be to God for dappled things—
　For skies of couple-colour as a brindled cow;
　　　For rose-moles all in stipple upon trout that swim;
Fresh-firecoal chestnut-falls; finches' wings;
　Landscape plotted and pieced—fold, fallow, and plough;
　　And all trades, their gear and tackle and trim.

All things counter, original, spare, strange;
　Whatever is fickle, freckled (who knows how?)
　　　With swift, slow; sweet, sour; adazzle, dim;
He fathers-forth whose beauty is past change:
　　Praise Him.

77　　THE FAIRIES

William Allingham
(1824-1889)

　Up the airy mountain,
　　Down the rushy glen,
　We daren't go a-hunting
　　For fear of little men;
　Wee folk, good folk,
　　Trooping all together;
　Green jackets, red cap,
　　And white owl's feather!

　Down along the rocky shore
　　Some make their home,
　They live on crispy pancakes
　　Of yellow tide-foam;
　Some in the reeds
　　Of the black mountain lake,
　With frogs for their watch-dogs,
　　All night awake.

High on the hill-top
    The old King sits;
He is now so old and gray
    He's nigh lost his wits.
With a bridge of white mist
    Columbkill he crosses,
On his stately journeys
    From Slieveleague to Rosses;
Or going up with music
    On cold starry nights
To sup with the Queen
    Of the gay Northern Lights.

They stole little Bridget
    For seven years long;
When she came down again
    Her friends were all gone.
They took her lightly back,
    Between the night and morrow;
They thought that she was fast asleep,
    But she was dead with sorrow.
They have kept her ever since
    Deep within the lake,
On a bed of flag-leaves,
    Watching till she wake.

By the craggy hill-side,
    Through the mosses bare,
They have planted thorn-trees
    For pleasure here and there.
If any man so daring
    As dig them up in spite,
He shall find their sharpest thorns
    In his bed at night.

Up the airy mountain,
    Down the rushy glen,
We daren't go a-hunting
    For fear of little men;
Wee folk, good folk,
    Trooping all together;
Green jacket, red cap,
    And white owl's feather!

78 HERACLITUS

W. J. Cory
(1823-1892)

They told me, Heraclitus, they told me you were dead,
They brought me bitter news to hear and bitter tears to shed.
I wept as I remembered how often you and I
Had tired the sun with talking and sent him down the sky.

And now that thou art lying, my dear old Carian guest,
A handful of grey ashes, long, long ago at rest,
Still are thy pleasant voices, thy nightingales, awake;
For Death, he taketh all away, but these he cannot take.

79 THE CHARGE OF THE LIGHT BRIGADE

Lord Tennyson
(1809-1892)

Half a league, half a league,
  Half a league onward,
All in the valley of Death
  Rode the six hundred.
'Forward, the Light Brigade!
Charge for the guns!' he said:
Into the valley of Death
  Rode the six hundred.

'Forward, the Light Brigade!'
Was there a man dismay'd?
Not tho' the soldier knew
  Someone had blunder'd:
Theirs not to make reply,
Theirs not to reason why,
Theirs but to do and die:
Into the valley of Death
  Rode the six hundred.

Cannon to right of them,
Cannon to left of them,
Cannon in front of them
    Volley'd and thunder'd;
Storm'd at with shot and shell,
Boldly they rode and well,
Into the jaws of Death,
Into the mouth of Hell
    Rode the six hundred.

Flash'd all their sabres bare,
Flash'd as they turn'd in air,
Sabring the gunners there,
Charging an army, while
    All the world wonder'd:
Plunged in the battery-smoke
Right thro' the line they broke;
Cossack and Russian
Reel'd from the sabre-stroke
Shatter'd and sunder'd.
Then they rode back, but not,
    Not the six hundred.

Cannon to right of them,
Cannon to left of them,
Cannon behind them
    Volley'd and thunder'd;
Storm'd at with shot and shell,
While horse and hero fell,
They that had fought so well
Came thro' the jaws of Death,
Back from the mouth of Hell,
All that was left of them,
    Left of six hundred.

When can their glory fade?
O the wild charge they made!
    All the world wonder'd.
Honour the charge they made!
Honour the Light Brigade,
    Noble six hundred!

THE LADY OF SHALOTT

Lord Tennyson

PART I

On either side the river lie
Long fields of barley and of rye,
That clothe the wold and meet the sky;
And thro' the field the road runs by
     To many-tower'd Camelot;
And up and down the people go,
Gazing where the lilies blow
Round an island there below,
     The island of Shalott.

Willows whiten, aspens quiver,
Little breezes dusk and shiver
Thro' the wave that runs for ever
By the island in the river
     Flowing down to Camelot.
Four grey walls, and four grey towers,
Overlook a space of flowers,
And the silent isle embowers
     The Lady of Shalott.

By the margin, willow-veil'd,
Slide the heavy barges trail'd
By slow horses; and unhail'd
The shallop flitteth silken-sail'd
     Skimming down to Camelot:
But who hath seen her wave her hand?
Or at the casement seen her stand?
Or is she known in all the land,
     The Lady of Shalott?

Only reapers, reaping early
In among the bearded barley,
Hear a song that echoes cheerly
From the river winding clearly,
     Down to tower'd Camelot:
And by the moon the reaper weary,
Piling sheaves in uplands airy,
Listening, whispers, ' 'Tis the fairy
     Lady of Shalott.'

PART II

There she weaves by night and day
A magic web with colours gay.
She has heard a whisper say,
A curse is on her if she stay
    To look down to Camelot.
She knows not what the curse may be,
And so she weaveth steadily,
And little other care hath she,
    The Lady of Shalott.

And moving thro' a mirror clear
That hangs before her all the year,
Shadows of the world appear.
There she sees the highway near
    Winding down to Camelot:
There the river eddy whirls,
And there the surly village-churls,
And the red cloaks of market girls,
    Pass onward from Shalott.

Sometimes a troop of damsels glad,
An abbot on an ambling pad,
Sometimes a curly shepherd-lad,
Or long-hair'd page in crimson clad,
    Goes by to tower'd Camelot;
And sometimes thro' the mirror blue
The knights come riding two and two:
She hath no loyal knight and true,
    The Lady of Shalott.

But in her web she still delights
To weave the mirror's magic sights,
For often thro' the silent nights
A funeral, with plumes and lights,
    And music, went to Camelot:
Or when the moon was overhead,
Came two young lovers lately wed:
'I am half sick of shadows,' said
    The Lady of Shalott.

Part III

A bow-shot from her bower-eaves,
He rode between the barley-sheaves,
The sun came dazzling thro' the leaves,
And flamed upon the brazen greaves
        Of bold Sir Lancelot.
A red-cross knight for ever kneel'd
To a lady in his shield,
That sparkled on the yellow field,
        Beside remote Shalott.

The gemmy bridle glitter'd free,
Like to some branch of stars we see
Hung in the golden Galaxy.
The bridle bells rang merrily
        As he rode down to Camelot:
And from his blazon'd baldric slung
A mighty silver bugle hung,
And as he rode his armour rung,
        Beside remote Shalott.

All in the blue unclouded weather
Thick-jewell'd shone the saddle-leather,
The helmet and the helmet-feather
Burn'd like one burning flame together,
        As he rode down to Camelot.
As often thro' the purple night,
Below the starry clusters bright,
Some bearded meteor, trailing light,
        Moves over still Shalott.

His broad clear brow in the sunlight glow'd;
On burnish'd hooves his war-horse trode;
From underneath his helmet flow'd
His coal-black curls as on he rode,
        As he rode down to Camelot.
From the bank and from the river
He flash'd into the crystal mirror,
'Tirra lirra,' by the river
        Sang Sir Lancelot.

She left the web, she left the loom,
She made three paces thro' the room,
She saw the water-lily bloom,
She saw the helmet and the plume,
　　She look'd down to Camelot.
Out flew the web and floated wide;
The mirror crack'd from side to side;
'The curse is come upon me,' cried
　　The Lady of Shalott.

PART IV

In the stormy east-wind straining,
The pale yellow woods were waning,
The broad stream in his banks complaining,
Heavily the low sky raining
　　Over tower'd Camelot;
Down she came and found a boat
Beneath a willow left afloat,
And round about the prow she wrote
　　The Lady of Shalott.

And down the river's dim expanse—
Like some bold seer in a trance,
Seeing all his own mischance—
With a glassy countenance
　　Did she look to Camelot.
And at the closing of the day
She loosed the chain, and down she lay;
The broad stream bore her far away,
　　The Lady of Shalott.

Lying, robed in snowy white
That loosely flew to left and right—
The leaves upon her falling light—
Thro' the noises of the night
　　She floated down to Camelot:
And as the boat-head wound along
The willowy hills and fields among,
They heard her singing her last song,
　　The Lady of Shalott.

Heard a carol, mournful, holy,
Chanted loudly, chanted lowly,
Till her blood was frozen slowly,
And her eyes were darken'd wholly,
    Turn'd to tower'd Camelot.
For ere she reach'd upon the tide
The first house by the water-side,
Singing in her song she died,
    The Lady of Shalott.

Under tower and balcony,
By garden-wall and gallery,
A gleaming shape she floated by,
Dead-pale between the houses high,
    Silent into Camelot,
Out upon the wharfs they came,
Knight and burgher, lord and dame,
And round the prow they read her name,
    The Lady of Shalott.

Who is this? And what is here?
And in the lighted palace near
Died the sound of royal cheer;
And they cross'd themselves for fear,
    All the knights at Camelot:
But Lancelot mused a little space;
He said, 'She has a lovely face;
God in His mercy lend her grace,
    The Lady of Shalott.'

81   THE SPLENDOUR FALLS ON CASTLE WALLS

Lord Tennyson

The splendour falls on castle walls
    And snowy summits old in story:
The long light shakes across the lakes,
    And the wild cataract leaps in glory.
Blow, bugle, blow, set the wild echoes flying,
Blow, bugle; answer, echoes, dying, dying, dying.

O hark, O hear! how thin and clear,
    And thinner, clearer, farther going!
O sweet and far from cliff and scar
    The horns of Elfland faintly blowing!
Blow, let us hear the purple glens replying:
Blow, bugle; answer, echoes, dying, dying, dying.

O love, they die in yon rich sky,
    They faint on hill or field or river:
Our echoes roll from soul to soul,
    And grow for ever and for ever.
Blow, bugle, blow, set the wild echoes flying,
And answer, echoes, answer, dying, dying, dying.

82   THE EAGLE

Lord Tennyson

He clasps the crag with crooked hands;
Close to the sun in lonely lands,
Ringed with the azure world, he stands.

The wrinkled sea beneath him crawls;
He watches from his mountain walls,
And like a thunderbolt he falls.

83   BREAK, BREAK, BREAK

Lord Tennyson

Break, break, break,
    On thy cold grey stones, O Sea!
And I would that my tongue could utter
    The thoughts that arise in me.

O well for the fisherman's boy,
    That he shouts with his sister at play!
O well for the sailor lad,
    That he sings in his boat on the bay!

And the stately ships go on
    To their haven under the hill;
But O for the touch of a vanish'd hand,
    And the sound of a voice that is still!

Break, break, break,
    At the foot of thy crags, O Sea!
But the tender grace of a day that is dead
    Will never come back to me.

84   THE BROOK

Lord Tennyson

I come from haunts of coot and hern,
    I make a sudden sally,
And sparkle out among the fern,
    To bicker down a valley.

By thirty hills I hurry down,
    Or slip between the ridges,
By twenty thorps, a little town,
    And half a hundred bridges.

Till last by Philip's farm I flow
    To join the brimming river,
For men may come and men may go,
    But I go on for ever.

I chatter over stony ways,
    In little sharps and trebles,
I bubble into eddying bays,
    I babble on the pebbles.

With many a curve my banks I fret
   By many a field and fallow,
And many a fairy foreland set
   With willow-weed and mallow.

I chatter, chatter, as I flow
   To join the brimming river,
For men may come and men may go,
   But I go on for ever.

I wind about, and in and out,
   With here a blossom sailing,
And here and there a lusty trout,
   And here and there a grayling.

And here and there a foamy flake
   Upon me, as I travel
With many a silvery waterbreak
   Above the golden gravel,

And draw them all along, and flow
   To join the brimming river,
For men may come and men may go,
   But I go on for ever.

I steal by lawns and grassy plots,
   I slide by hazel covers;
I move the sweet forget-me-nots
   That grow for happy lovers.

I slip, I slide, I gloom, I glance,
   Among my skimming swallows;
I make the netted sunbeams dance
   Against my sandy shallows.

I murmur under moon and stars
   In brambly wildernesses;
I linger by my shingly bars;
   I loiter round my cresses;

And out again I curve and flow
   To join the brimming river,
For men may come and men may go,
   But I go on for ever.

85 CROSSING THE BAR

Lord Tennyson

Sunset and evening star,
  And one clear call for me!
And may there be no moaning of the bar,
  When I put out to sea.

But such a tide as moving seems asleep,
  Too full for sound and foam,
When that which drew from out the boundless deep
  Turns again home.

Twilight and evening bell,
  And after that the dark!
And may there be no sadness of farewell,
  When I embark;

For tho' from out our bourne of Time and Place
  The flood may bear me far,
I hope to see my Pilot face to face
  When I have crossed the bar.

86 UP-HILL

Christina Rossetti
(1830-1894)

Does the road wind up-hill all the way?
  Yes, to the very end.
Will the day's journey take the whole long day?
  From morn to night, my friend.

But is there for the night a resting-place?
   A roof for when the slow, dark hours begin.
May not the darkness hide it from my face?
   You cannot miss that inn.

Shall I meet other wayfarers at night?
   Those who have gone before.
Then must I knock, or call when just in sight?
   They will not keep you waiting at that door.

Shall I find comfort, travel-sore and weak?
   Of labour you shall find the sum.
Will there be beds for me and all who seek?
   Yea, beds for all who come.

87   SING ME A SONG OF A LAD THAT IS GONE

Robert Louis Stevenson
(1850-1894)

Sing me a song of a lad that is gone,
   Say, could that lad be I?
Merry of soul he sailed on a day
   Over the sea to Skye.

Mull was astern, Rum on the port,
   Eigg on the starboard bow;
Glory of youth glowed in his soul:
   Where is that glory now?

Sing me a song of a lad that is gone,
   Say, could that lad be I?
Merry of soul he sailed on a day
   Over the sea to Skye.

Give me again all that was there,
    Give me the sun that shone!
Give me the eyes, give me the soul,
    Give me the lad that's gone!

Sing me a song of a lad that is gone,
    Say, could that lad be I?
Merry of soul he sailed on a day
    Over the sea to Skye.

Billow and breeze, islands and seas,
    Mountains of rain and sun,
All that was good, all that was fair,
    All that was me is gone.

88   REQUIEM

Robert Louis Stevenson

Under the wide and starry sky,
Dig the grave and let me lie.
Glad did I live and gladly die,
    And I laid me down with a will.

This be the verse you grave for me:
Here he lies where he longed to be;
Home is the sailor, home from sea,
    And the hunter home from the hill.

89 THE HIGH TIDE ON THE COAST OF LINCOLNSHIRE (1571)

Jean Ingelow
(1820-1897)

The old mayor climbed the belfry tower,
   The ringers ran by two, by three;
'Pull, if ye never pulled before;
   Good ringers, pull your best,' quoth he.
'Play up, play up, O Boston bells!
Play all your changes, all your swells,
   Play up "The Brides of Enderby".'

Men say it was a stolen tide—
   The Lord that sent it, He knows all;
But in mine ears doth still abide
   The message that the bells let fall:
And there was nought of strange, beside
The flights of mews and peewits pied
   By millions crouched on the old sea wall.

I sat and spun within the door,
   My thread brake off, I raised mine eyes;
The level sun, like ruddy ore,
   Lay sinking in the barren skies,
And dark against day's golden death
She moved where Lindis wandereth,
   My son's fair wife, Elizabeth.

'Cusha! Cusha! Cusha!' calling,
Ere the early dews were falling,
   Far away I heard her song.
'Cusha! Cusha!' all along
Where the reedy Lindis floweth,
     Floweth, floweth;
From the meads where melick groweth
Faintly came her milking song—

'Cusha! Cusha! Cusha!' calling,
'For the dews will soon be falling;
Leave your meadow grasses mellow,
    Mellow, mellow;
Quit your cowslips, cowslips yellow;
Come up, Whitefoot, come up, Lightfoot;
Quit the stalks of parsley hollow,
    Hollow, hollow;
Come up, Jetty, rise and follow,
    From the clovers lift your head;
Come up, Whitefoot, come up, Lightfoot,
Come up, Jetty, rise and follow,
    Jetty, to the milking shed.'

If it be long, ay, long ago,
    When I begin to think how long,
Again I hear the Lindis flow,
    Swift as an arrow, sharp and strong;
And all the air, it seemeth me,
Bin full of floating bells (saith she),
That ring the tune of Enderby.

All fresh the level pasture lay,
    And not a shadow might be seen,
Save where full five good miles away
    The steeple towered from out the green;
And lo! the great bell far and wide
Was heard in all the countryside
That Saturday at eventide.

The swanherds where their sedges are
    Moved on in sunset's golden breath,
The shepherd lads I heard afar,
    And my son's wife, Elizabeth;
Till floating o'er the grassy sea
Came down the kindly message free,
The 'Brides of Mavis Enderby'.

Then some looked up into the sky,
    And all along where Lindis flows
To where the goodly vessels lie,
    And where the lordly steeple shows.

They said, 'And why should this thing be?
What danger lowers by land or sea?
They ring the tune of Enderby!

'For evil news from Mablethorpe,
    Of pirate galleys warping down;
For ships ashore beyond the scorpe,
    They have not spared to wake the town;
But while the west bin red to see,
And storms be none, and pirates flee,
Why ring "The Brides of Enderby"?'

I looked without, and lo! my son
    Came riding down with might and main:
He raised a shout as he drew on,
    Till all the welkin rang again,
'Elizabeth! Elizabeth!'
(A sweeter woman ne'er drew breath
Than my son's wife, Elizabeth.)

'The old sea wall (he cried) is down,
    The rising tide comes on apace,
And boats adrift in yonder town
    Go sailing up the market-place.'
He shook as one that looks on death:
'God save you, mother!' straight he saith;
'Where is my wife, Elizabeth?'

'Good son, where Lindis winds her way,
    With her two bairns I marked her long;
And ere yon bells began to play
    Afar I heard her milking song.'
He looked across the grassy lea,
To right, to left, 'Ho, Enderby!'
They rang 'The Brides of Enderby!'

With that he cried and beat his breast;
For lo! along the river's bed
A mighty eygre reared his crest,
    And up the Lindis raging sped.
It swept with thunderous noises loud;
Shaped like a curling snow-white cloud,
Or like a demon in a shroud.

112

And rearing Lindis backward pressed
    Shook all her trembling banks amain;
Then madly at the eygre's breast
    Flung up her weltering walls again.
Then banks came down with ruin and rout—
Then beaten foam flew round about—
Then all the mighty floods were out.

So far, so fast the eygre drave,
    The heart had hardly time to beat,
Before a shallow seething wave
    Sobbed in the grasses at our feet:
The feet had hardly time to flee
Before it broke against the knee,
And all the world was in the sea.

Upon the roof we sat that night,
    The noise of bells went sweeping by;
I marked the lofty beacon light
    Stream from the church tower, red and high—
A lurid mark and dread to see;
And awesome bells they were to me,
That in the dark rang 'Enderby'.

They rang, the sailor lads to guide
    From roof to roof who fearless rowed;
And I—my son was at my side,
    And yet the ruddy beacon glowed;
And yet he moaned beneath his breath,
'O come in life, or come in death!
O lost! my love, Elizabeth.'

And didst thou visit him no more?
    Thou didst, thou didst, my daughter dear;
The waters laid thee at his door,
    Ere yet the early dawn was clear.
Thy pretty bairns in fast embrace,
The lifted sun shone on thy face,
Down drifted to thy dwelling-place.

That flow strewed wrecks about the grass,
    That ebb swept out the flocks to sea;
A fatal ebb and flow, alas!
    To many more than mine and me;
But each will mourn his own (she saith),
And sweeter woman ne'er drew breath
Than my son's wife, Elizabeth.

I shall never hear her more
By the reedy Lindis shore,
'Cusha! Cusha! Cusha!' calling,
Ere the early dews be falling;
I shall never hear her song,
'Cusha! Cusha!' all along
Where the sunny Lindis floweth,
    Goeth, floweth;
From the meads where melick groweth,
When the water winding down,
Onward floweth to the town.

I shall never see her more
Where the reeds and rushes quiver,
    Shiver, quiver;
Stand beside the sobbing river,
Sobbing, throbbing, in its falling
To the sandy lonesome shore;
I shall never hear her calling,
'Leave your meadow grasses mellow,
    Mellow, mellow;
Quit your cowslips, cowslips yellow;
Come up, Whitefoot, come up, Lightfoot;
Quit your pipes of parsley hollow,
    Hollow, hollow;
Come up, Lightfoot, rise and follow;
    Lightfoot, Whitefoot,
From your clovers lift the head;
Come up, Jetty, follow, follow,
    Jetty, to the milking shed.'

HE THOUGHT HE SAW

Lewis Carroll
(*1832-1898*)

He thought he saw an Elephant,
    That practised on a fife:
He looked again, and found it was
    A letter from his wife.
'At length I realise,' he said,
    'The bitterness of Life!'

He thought he saw a Buffalo
    Upon the chimney-piece:
He looked again, and found it was
    His Sister's Husband's Niece.
'Unless you leave this house,' he said,
    'I'll send for the police!'

He thought he saw a Rattlesnake
    That questioned him in Greek:
He looked again, and found it was
    The Middle of Next Week.
'The one thing I regret,' he said,
    'Is that it cannot speak!'

He thought he saw a Banker's Clerk
    Descending from the bus:
He looked again, and found it was
    A Hippopotamus:
'If this should stay to dine,' he said,
    'There won't be much for us!'

He thought he saw a Kangaroo
    That worked a coffee-mill:
He looked again, and found it was
    A Vegetable-Pill.
'Were I to swallow this,' he said,
    'I should be very ill!'

He thought he saw a Coach-and-Four
    That stood beside his bed:
He looked again, and found it was
    A bear without a Head.
'Poor thing,' he said, 'poor silly thing!
    It's waiting to be fed!'

He thought he saw an Albatross
    That fluttered round the lamp:
He looked again, and found it was
    A Penny-Postage-Stamp.
'You'd best be getting home,' he said,
    'The nights are very damp!'

He thought he saw a Garden-Door
    That opened with a key:
He looked again, and found it was
    A Double Rule of Three.
'And all its mystery,' he said,
    'Is clear as day to me!'

He thought he saw an Argument
    That proved he was the Pope:
He looked again, and found it was
    A Bar of Mottled Soap.
'A fact so dread,' he faintly said,
    'Extinguishes all hope!'

91   FATHER WILLIAM

Lewis Carroll

'You are old, Father William,' the young man said,
    'And your hair has become very white;
And yet you incessantly stand on your head—
    Do you think, at your age, it is right?'

'In my youth,' Father William replied to his son,
    'I feared it might injure the brain;
But, now that I'm perfectly sure I have none,
    Why, I do it again and again.'

'You are old,' said the youth, 'as I mentioned before,
    And have grown most uncommonly fat;
Yet you turned a back-somersault in at the door—
    Pray, what is the reason of that?'

'In my youth,' said the sage, as he shook his grey locks,
    'I kept all my limbs very supple
By the use of this ointment—one shilling the box—
    Allow me to sell you a couple?'

'You are old,' said the youth, 'and your jaws are too weak
    For anything tougher than suet;
Yet you finished the goose, with the bones and the beak—
    Pray, how did you manage to do it?'

'In my youth,' said his father, 'I took to the law,
    And argued each case with my wife;
And the muscular strength, which it gave to my jaw,
    Has lasted the rest of my life.'

'You are old,' said the youth, 'one would hardly suppose
    That your eye was as steady as ever;
Yet you balanced an eel on the end of your nose—
    What made you so awfully clever?'

'I have answered three questions, and that is enough,'
    Said his father; 'don't give yourself airs!
Do you think I can listen all day to such stuff?
    Be off, or I'll kick you downstairs!'

92 THE WALRUS AND THE CARPENTER

Lewis Carroll

The sun was shining on the sea,
    Shining with all his might:
He did his very best to make
    The billows smooth and bright—
And this was very odd, because it was
    The middle of the night.

The moon was shining sulkily,
    Because she thought the sun
Had got no business to be there
    After the day was done—
'It's very rude of him,' she said,
    'To come and spoil the fun!'

The sea was wet as wet could be,
    The sands were dry as dry.
You could not see a cloud, because
    No cloud was in the sky:
No birds were flying overhead—
    There were no birds to fly.

The Walrus and the Carpenter
    Were walking close at hand;
They wept like anything to see
    Such quantities of sand:
'If this were only cleared away,'
    They said, 'it would be grand!'

'If seven maids with seven mops
    Swept it for half a year,
Do you suppose,' the Walrus said,
    'That they would get it clear?'
'I doubt it,' said the Carpenter,
    And shed a bitter tear.

'O Oysters, come and walk with us!'
    The Walrus did beseech.
'A pleasant walk, a pleasant talk,
    Along the briny beach:
We cannot do with more than four,
    To give a hand to each.'

The eldest Oyster looked at him,
    But never a word he said:
The eldest Oyster winked his eye,
    And shook his heavy head—
Meaning to say he did not choose
    To leave the oyster-bed.

But four young Oysters hurried up,
    All eager for the treat:
Their coats were brushed, their faces washed,
    Their shoes were clean and neat—
And this was odd, because, you know,
    They hadn't any feet.

Four other Oysters followed them,
    And yet another four;
And thick and fast they came at last,
    And more, and more, and more—
All hopping through the frothy waves,
    And scrambling to the shore.

The Walrus and the Carpenter
    Walked on a mile or so,
And then they rested on a rock
    Conveniently low:
And all the little Oysters stood
    And waited in a row.

'The time has come,' the Walrus said,
    'To talk of many things:
Of shoes—and ships—and sealing wax—
    Of cabbages—and kings—
And why the sea is boiling hot—
    And whether pigs have wings.'

'But wait a bit,' the Oysters cried,
    'Before we have our chat;
For some of us are out of breath,
    And all of us are fat!'
'No hurry!' said the Carpenter.
    They thanked him much for that.

'A loaf of bread,' the Walrus said,
    'Is what we chiefly need;
Pepper and vinegar besides
    Are very good indeed—
Now, if you're ready, Oysters dear,
    We can begin to feed.'

'But not on us,' the Oysters cried,
    Turning a little blue.
'After such kindness that would be
    A dismal thing to do!'
'The night is fine,' the Walrus said,
    'Do you admire the view?

'It was so kind of you to come,
    And you are very nice!'
The Carpenter said nothing but,
    'Cut us another slice.
I wish you were not quite so deaf—
    I've had to ask you twice!'

'It seems a shame,' the Walrus said,
    'To play them such a trick.
After we've brought them out so far
    And made them trot so quick!'
The Carpenter said nothing but,
    'The butter's spread too thick!'

'I weep for you,' the Walrus said,
    'I deeply sympathise.'
With sobs and tears he sorted out
    Those of the largest size,
Holding his pocket-handkerchief
    Before his streaming eyes.

'O Oysters,' said the Carpenter,
    'You've had a pleasant run!
Shall we be trotting home again?'
    But answer came there none—
And this was scarcely odd, because
    They'd eaten every one.

93   OUT OF THE NIGHT THAT
COVERS ME

W. E. Henley
(1849-1903)

Out of the night that covers me,
    Black as the pit from pole to pole,
I thank whatever gods may be
    For my unconquerable soul.

In the fell clutch of circumstance
    I have not winced nor cried aloud.
Under the bludgeonings of chance
    My head is bloody, but unbow'd.

Beyond this place of wrath and tears
    Looms but the Horror of the shade,
And yet the menace of the years
    Finds, and shall find, me unafraid.

It matters not how strait the gate,
    How charged with punishments the scroll,
I am the master of my fate;
    I am the captain of my soul.

IN NO STRANGE LAND

Francis Thompson
(1859-1907)

O world invisible, we view thee,
O world intangible, we touch thee,
O world unknowable, we know thee,
Inapprehensible, we clutch thee!

Does the fish soar to find the ocean,
The eagle plunge to find the air—
That we ask of the stars in motion
If they have rumour of thee there?

Not where the wheeling systems darken,
And our benumbed conceiving soars!—
The drift of pinions, would we hearken,
Beats at our own clay-shuttered doors.

The angels keep their ancient places:—
Turn but a stone, and start a wing!
'Tis ye, 'tis your estrangèd faces,
That miss the many-splendoured thing.

But (when so sad thou canst not sadder)
Cry;—and upon thy so sore loss
Shall shine the traffic of Jacob's ladder
Pitched betwixt Heaven and Charing Cross.

Yea, in the night, my Soul, my daughter,
Cry,—clinging Heaven by the hems;
And lo, Christ walking on the water,
Not of Gennesaret, but Thames!

A RUNNABLE STAG

John Davidson
(1857-1909)

When pods went pop on the broom, green broom,
  And apples began to be golden-skinned,
We harboured a stag in the Priory coomb,
  And we feathered his trail up-wind, up-wind,
  We feathered his trail up-wind—
    A stag of warrant, a stag, a stag,
    A runnable stag, a kingly crop,
    Brow, bay and tray and three on top,
    A stag, a runnable stag.

Then the huntsman's horn rang yap, yap, yap,
  And 'Forwards' we heard the harbourer shout;
But 'twas only a brocket that broke a gap
  In the beechen underwood, driven out,
  From the underwood antlered out
    By warrant and might of the stag, the stag,
    The runnable stag, whose lordly mind
    Was bent on sleep, though beamed and tined
    He stood, a runnable stag.

So we tufted the covert till afternoon
  With Tinkerman's Pup and Bell-of-the-North;
And hunters were sulky and hounds out of tune
  Before we tufted the right stag forth,
  Before we tufted him forth,
    The stag of warrant, the wily stag,
    The runnable stag with his kingly crop,
    Brow, bay and tray and three on top,
    The royal and runnable stag.

It was Bell-of-the-North and Tinkerman's Pup
  That stuck to the scent till the copse was drawn.
'Tally ho! tally ho!' and the hunt was up,
  The tufters whipped and the pack laid on,
  The resolute pack laid on,
    And the stag of warrant away at last,
    The runnable stag, the same, the same,
    His hoofs on fire, his horns like flame,
    A stag, a runnable stag.

'Let your gelding be: if you check or chide
　　He stumbles at once and you're out of the hunt;
For three hundred gentlemen, able to ride,
　　On hunters accustomed to bear the brunt,
　　Accustomed to bear the brunt,
　　　　Are after the runnable stag, the stag,
　　　　The runnable stag, with his kingly crop,
　　　　Brow, bay and tray and three on top,
　　　　The right, the runnable stag.'

By perilous paths in coomb and dell,
　　The heather, the rocks, and the river-bed,
The pace grew hot, for the scent lay well,
　　And a runnable stag goes right ahead,
　　The quarry went right ahead—
　　　　Ahead, ahead, and fast and far;
　　　　His antlered crest, his cloven hoof,
　　　　Brow, bay and tray and three aloof,
　　　　The stag, the runnable stag.

For a matter of twenty miles and more,
　　By the densest hedge and the highest wall,
Through herds of bullocks he baffled the lore
　　Of harbourer, huntsman, hounds and all,
　　Of harbourer, hounds and all—
　　　　The stag of warrant, the wily stag,
　　　　For twenty miles, and five and five,
　　　　He ran, and he never was caught alive,
　　　　This stag, this runnable stag.

When he turned at bay in the leafy gloom,
　　In the emerald gloom where the brook ran deep,
He heard in the distance the rollers boom,
　　And he saw in a vision of peaceful sleep,
　　In a wonderful vision of sleep,
　　　　A stag of warrant, a stag, a stag,
　　　　A runnable stag in a jewelled bed,
　　　　Under the sheltering ocean dead,
　　　　A stag, a runnable stag.

So a fateful hope lit up his eye,
    And he opened his nostrils wide again,
And he tossed his branching antlers high
       As he headed the hunt down the Charlock glen,
       As he raced down the echoing glen
          For five miles more, the stag, the stag,
          For twenty miles, and five and five,
          Not to be caught now, dead or alive,
          The stag, the runnable stag.

Three hundred gentlemen, able to ride,
    Three hundred horses as gallant and free,
Beheld him escape on the evening tide,
       Far out till he sank in the Severn Sea,
       Till he sank in the depths of the sea—
          The stag, the buoyant stag, the stag
          That slept at last in a jewelled bed
          Under the sheltering ocean spread,
          The stag, the runnable stag.

96   THE SOLDIER

Rupert Brooke
(1887-1915)

If I should die, think only this of me:
    That there's some corner of a foreign field
That is for ever England.   There shall be
    In that rich earth a richer dust concealed;
A dust whom England bore, shaped, made aware,
    Gave, once, her flowers to love, her ways to roam,
A body of England's, breathing English air,
    Washed by the rivers, blest by suns of home.

And think, this heart, all evil shed away,
    A pulse in the eternal mind, no less
    Gives somewhere back the thoughts by England given;
Her sights and sounds; dreams happy as her day;
    And laughter, learnt of friends; and gentleness,
    In hearts at peace, under an English heaven.

THE OLD SHIPS

James Elroy Flecker
(1884-1915)

I have seen old ships sail like swans asleep
Beyond the village which men still call Tyre,
With leaden age o'ercargoed, dipping deep
For Famagusta and the hidden sun
That rings black Cyprus with a lake of fire;
And all those ships were certainly so old—
Who knows how oft with squat and noisy gun,
Questing brown slaves or Syrian oranges,
The pirate Genoese
Hell-raked them till they rolled
Blood, water, fruit and corpses up the hold.
But now through friendly seas they softly run,
Painted the mid-sea blue or shore-sea green,
Still patterned with the vine and grapes in gold.

But I have seen
Pointing her shapely shadows from the dawn
An image tumbled on a rose-swept bay,
A drowsy ship of some yet older day;
And, wonder's breath indrawn,
Thought I—who knows—who knows—but in that same
(Fished up beyond Aegaea, patched up new
—Stern painted brighter blue—)
That talkative, bald-headed seaman came
(Twelve patient comrades sweating at the oar)
From Troy's doom-crimson shore,
And with great lies about his wooden horse
Set the crew laughing, and forgot his course.

It was so old a ship—who knows, who knows?
—And yet so beautiful, I watched in vain
To see the mast burst open with a rose,
And the whole deck put on its leaves again.

INTO BATTLE

Julian Grenfell
(1888-1915)

The naked earth is warm with spring,
    And with green grass and bursting trees
Leans to the sun's gaze glorying,
    And quivers in the sunny breeze;
And life is colour and warmth and light,
    And a striving evermore for these;
And he is dead who will not fight;
    And who dies fighting has increase.

The fighting man shall from the sun
    Take warmth, and life from the glowing earth;
Speed with the light-foot winds to run,
    And with the trees to newer birth;
And find, when fighting shall be done,
    Great rest, and fullness after dearth.

All the bright company of Heaven
    Hold him in their high comradeship,
The Dog-Star, and the Sisters Seven,
    Orion's Belt and sworded hip.

The woodland trees that stand together,
    They stand to him each one a friend;
They gently speak in the windy weather:
    They guide to valley and ridge's end.

The kestrel hovering by day,
    And the little owls that call by night,
Bid him be swift and keen as they,
    As keen of ear, as swift of sight.

The blackbird sings to him, 'Brother, brother,
    If this be the last song you shall sing,
Sing well, for you may not sing another;
    Brother, sing.'

In dreary, doubtful, waiting hours,
    Before the brazen frenzy starts,
The horses show him nobler powers;
    O patient eyes, courageous hearts!

And when the burning moment breaks,
    And all things else are out of mind,
And only joy of battle takes
    Him by the throat, and makes him blind,

Through joy and blindness he shall know,
    Not caring much to know, that still
Nor lead nor steel shall reach him, so
    That it be not the Destined Will.

The thundering line of battle stands,
    And in the air Death moans and sings;
But Day shall clasp him with strong hands,
    And Night shall fold him in soft wings.

99   LIGHTS OUT

Edward Thomas
(1878-1917)

I have come to the borders of sleep,
The unfathomable deep
Forest where all must lose
Their way, however straight,
Or winding, soon or late;
They cannot choose.

Many a road and track
That, since the dawn's first crack,
Up to the forest brink,
Deceived the travellers,
Suddenly now blurs,
And in they sink.

Here love ends,
Despair, ambition ends,
All pleasure and all trouble,
Although most sweet or bitter,
Here ends in sleep that is sweeter
Than tasks most noble.

128

There is not any book,
Or face of dearest look,
That I would not turn from now,
To go into the unknown.
I must enter and leave alone,
I know not how.

The tall forest towers;
Its cloudy foliage lowers
Ahead, shelf above shelf;
Its silence I hear and obey
That I may lose my way
And myself.

100 ANTHEM FOR DOOMED YOUTH

Wilfred Owen
(1893-1918)

What passing-bells for these who die as cattle?
    Only the monstrous anger of the guns;
Only the stuttering rifles' rapid rattle
    Can patter out their hasty orisons.
No mockeries for them from prayers or bells,
    Nor any voice of mourning save the choirs,—
The shrill, demented choirs of wailing shells;
    And bugles calling for them from sad shires.

What candles may be held to speed them all?
    Not in the hands of boys, but in their eyes
Shall shine the holy glimmers of good-byes.
    The pallor of girls' brows shall be their pall;
Their flowers the tenderness of patient minds,
And each slow dusk a drawing-down of blinds.

101 WEATHERS

Thomas Hardy
(1840-1928)

This is the weather the cuckoo likes,
        And so do I;
When showers betumble the chestnut spikes,
        And nestlings fly:
And the little brown nightingale bills his best,
And they sit outside at 'The Travellers' Rest',
And maids come forth sprig-muslin drest,
And citizens dream of the south and west,
        And so do I.

This is the weather the shepherd shuns,
        And so do I;
When beeches drip in browns and duns,
        And thresh, and ply;
And hill-hid tides throb, throe on throe,
And meadow rivulets overflow,
And drops on gate-bars hang in a row,
And rooks in families homeward go,
        And so do I.

102 THE OXEN

Thomas Hardy

Christmas Eve, and twelve of the clock.
    'Now they are all on their knees,'
An elder said as we sat in a flock
    By the embers in hearthside ease.

We pictured the meek mild creatures where
   They dwelt in their strawy pen,
Nor did it occur to one of us there
   To doubt they were kneeling then.

So fair a fancy few would weave
   In these years! Yet, I feel,
If some one said on Christmas Eve,
   'Come; see the oxen kneel

In the lonely barton by yonder coomb
   Our childhood used to know,'
I should go with him in the gloom,
   Hoping it might be so.

103   LONDON SNOW

Robert Bridges
(1844-1930)

When men were all asleep the snow came flying,
   In large white flakes falling on the city brown,
Stealthily and perpetually settling and loosely lying,
   Hushing the latest traffic of the drowsy town;
Deadening, muffling, stifling its murmurs failing;
   Lazily and incessantly floating down and down:
Silently sifting and veiling road, roof and railing;
Hiding difference, making unevenness even,
   Into angles and crevices softly drifting and sailing.
   All night it fell, and when full inches seven
It lay in the depths of its uncompacted lightness,
   The clouds blew off from a high and frosty heaven;
   And all woke earlier for the unaccustomed brightness
Of the winter dawning, the strange unheavenly glare:
The eye marvelled—marvelled at the dazzling whiteness;
   The ear hearkened to the stillness of the solemn air;
No sound of wheel rumbling nor of foot falling,
And the busy morning cries came thin and spare.

Then boys I heard, as they went to school, calling,
They gathered up the crystal manna to freeze
Their tongues with tasting, their hands with snowballing;
　　Or rioted in a drift, plunging up to the knees;
Or peering up from under the white-mossed wonder,
'O look at the trees!' they cried, 'O look at the trees!'
　　With lessened load a few carts creak and blunder,
Following along the white deserted way,
A country company long dispersed asunder:
　　When now already the sun, in pale display,
Standing by Paul's high dome, spread forth below
His sparkling beams, and awoke the stir of day.
　　For now doors open, and war is waged with the snow;
And trains of sombre men, past tale of number,
Tread long brown paths, as toward their toil they go;
　　But even for them awhile no cares encumber
Their minds diverted; the daily word is unspoken,
The daily thoughts of labour and sorrow slumber
　　At the sight of the beauty that greets them, for the charm
　　　　　　　　　　　　　　　　　they have broken.

104　　　　　　　SNAKE

D. H. Lawrence
(1885-1930)

A snake came to my water-trough
On a hot, hot day, and I in pyjamas for the heat,
To drink there.

In the deep, strange-scented shade of the great dark
　　　　　　　　　　　　　　　　　carob-tree
I came down the steps with my pitcher
And must wait, must stand and wait, for there he was at
　　　　　　　　　　　　　　　the trough before me.

132

He reached down from a fissure in the earth-wall in the gloom
And trailed his yellow-brown slackness soft-bellied down,
>over the edge of the stone trough
And rested his throat upon the stone bottom,
And where the water had dripped from the tap, in a
>small clearness,
He sipped with his straight mouth,
Softly drank through his straight gums, into his slack
>long body,
Silently.

Someone was before me at my water-trough,
And I, like a second comer, waiting.

He lifted his head from his drinking, as cattle do,
And looked at me vaguely, as drinking cattle do,
And flickered his two-forked tongue from his lips, and
>mused a moment,
And stooped and drank a little more,
Being earth-brown, earth-golden from the
>burning bowels of the earth,
On the day of Sicilian July, with Etna smoking.

The voice of my education said to me
He must be killed,
For in Sicily the black, black snakes are innocent, the
>gold are venomous.

And voices in me said, if you were a man
You would take a stick and break him now, and finish
>him off.

But must I confess how I liked him,
How glad I was he had come like a guest in quiet, to
>drink at my water-trough
And depart peaceful, pacified, and thankless,
Into the burning bowels of this earth.

Was it cowardice, that I dared not kill him?
Was it perversity, that I longed to talk to him?
Was it humility to feel so honoured?
I felt so honoured.

And yet those voices:
If you were not afraid, you would kill him!

And truly I was afraid, I was most afraid,
But even so, honoured still more
That he should seek my hospitality
From out the dark door of the secret earth.

He drank enough
And lifted his head, dreamily, as one who has drunken,
And flickered his tongue like a forked night on the air,
                                      so black,
Seeming to lick his lips,
And looked around like a god, unseeing, into the air,
And slowly turned his head,
And slowly, very slowly, as if thrice adream,
Proceeded to draw his slow length curving round
And climb again the broken bank of my wall-face.

And as he put his head into that dreadful hole,
And as he slowly drew up, snake-easing his shoulders,
                            and entered farther,
A sort of horror, a sort of protest against his withdrawing
                          into that horrid black hole,
Deliberately going into the blackness, and slowly drawing
                          himself after,
Overcame me now his back was turned.

I looked around, I put down my pitcher,
I picked up a clumsy log
And threw it at the water-trough with a clatter.

I think it did not hit him,
But suddenly that part of him that was left behind
                          convulsed in undignified haste,
Writhed like lightning, and was gone
Into the black hole, the earth-lipped fissure in the wall-front,
At which, in the intense still noon, I stared with fascination.

And immediately I regretted it.
I thought how paltry, how vulgar, what a mean act!
I despised myself and the voices of my accursed human
                          education.

And I thought of the albatross,
And I wished he would come back, my snake.

For he seemed to me again like a king,
Like a king in exile, uncrowned in the underworld,
Now due to be crowned again.

And so, I missed my chance with one of the lords
Of life.
And I have something to expiate;
A pettiness.

105   THE DUCKS

Kenneth Grahame
(*1859-1932*)

All along the backwater,
Through the rushes tall,
Ducks are a-dabbling,
    Up tails all!

Ducks' tails, drakes' tails,
Yellow feet a-quiver,
Yellow bills all out of sight
    Busy in the river!

Slushy green undergrowth
Where the roach swim—
Here we keep our larder
    Cool and full and dim!

Every one for what he likes!
We like to be
Heads down, tails up,
    Dabbling free!

High in the blue above
Swifts whirl and call—
We are down a-dabbling,
    Up tails all!

Rudyard Kipling
(1865-1936)

You may talk o' gin and beer
When you're quartered safe out 'ere
An' you're sent to penny-fights an' Aldershot it;
But when it comes to slaughter
You will do your work on water,
An' you'll lick the bloomin' boots of 'im that's got it.
Now in Injia's sunny clime,
Where I used to spend my time
A-servin' of 'Er Majesty the Queen,
Of all them blackfaced crew
The finest man I knew
Was our regimental bhisti, Gunga Din.
        He was, 'Din! Din! Din!
  'You limpin' lump o' brick-dust, Gunga Din!
      'Hi! Slippy *hitherao!*
      'Water, get it! *Panee lao,*
  'You squidgy-nosed old idol, Gunga Din.'

The uniform 'e wore
Was nothin' much before,
An' rather less than 'arf o' that be'ind,
For a piece o' twisty rag
An' a goatskin water-bag
Was all the field-equipment 'e could find.
When the sweatin' troop-train lay
In a sidin' through the day,
Where the 'eat would make your bloomin' eyebrows crawl,
We shouted 'Harry By!'
Till our throats were bricky-dry,
Then we wopped 'im 'cause 'e couldn't serve us all.
        It was 'Din! Din! Din!
  'You 'eathen, where the mischief 'ave you been?
      'You put some *juldee* in it
      'Or I'll marrow you this minute
  'If you don't fill up my helmet, Gunga Din!'

'E would dot an' carry one
Till the longest day was done;
An' 'e didn't seem to know the use o' fear.
If we charged or broke or cut,
You could bet your bloomin' nut,
'E'd be waitin' fifty paces right flank rear.
With 'is mussick on 'is back,
'E would skip with our attack,
An' watch us till the bugles made 'Retire,'
An' for all 'is dirty 'ide
'E was white, clear white, inside
When 'e went to tend the wounded under fire!
        It was 'Din! Din! Din!'
   With the bullets kickin' dust-spots on the green.
      When the cartridges ran out,
      You could hear the front-ranks shout,
  'Hi! ammunition-mules an' Gunga Din!'

I shan't forgit the night
When I dropped be'ind the fight
With a bullet where my belt-plate should 'a' been.
I was chokin' mad with thirst,
An' the man that spied me first
Was our good old grinnin', gruntin' Gunga Din.
'E lifted up my 'ead,
An' 'e plugged me where I bled,
An' 'e gub me 'arf-a-pint o' water green.
It was crawlin' and it stunk,
But of all the drinks I've drunk,
I'm gratefullest to one from Gunga Din.
        It was 'Din! Din! Din!
   "Ere's a beggar with a bullet through 'is spleen;
      "E's chawin' up the ground,
      'An' 'e's kickin all around:
  'For Gawd's sake git the water, Gunga Din!'

'E carried me away
To where a dooli lay,
An' a bullet come an' drilled the beggar clean.
'E put me safe inside,
An' just before 'e died,
'I 'ope you liked your drink,' sez Gunga Din.

137

So I'll meet 'im later on
At the place where 'e is gone—
Where it's always double drill and no canteen.
'E'll be squattin' on the coals
Givin' drink to poor damned souls,
An' I'll get a swig in hell from Gunga Din!
    Yes, Din! Din! Din!
You Lazarushian-leather Gunga Din!
    Though I've belted you and flayed you,
    By the livin' Gawd that made you,
You're a better man than I am, Gunga Din.

107   RECESSIONAL

Rudyard Kipling

God of our fathers, known of old,
    Lord of our far-flung battle-line,
Beneath whose awful Hand we hold
    Dominion over palm and pine—
Lord God of Hosts, be with us yet,
Lest we forget—lest we forget!

The tumult and the shouting dies;
    The captains and the kings depart;
Still stands Thine ancient sacrifice,
    An humble and a contrite heart.
Lord God of Hosts, be with us yet,
Lest we forget—lest we forget!

Far-called, our navies melt away;
    On dune and headland sinks the fire;
Lo, all our pomp of yesterday
    Is one with Nineveh and Tyre!
Judge of the Nations, spare us yet,
Lest we forget—lest we forget!

If, drunk with sight of power, we loose
    Wild tongues that have not Thee in awe,
Such boastings as the Gentiles use,
    Or lesser breeds without the Law—
Lord God of Hosts, be with us yet,
Lest we forget—lest we forget!

For heathen heart that puts her trust
    In reeking tube and iron shard,
All valiant dust that builds on dust,
    And guarding calls not Thee to guard;
For frantic boast and foolish word—
Thy Mercy on Thy People, Lord!

108   **IF—**

Rudyard Kipling

If you can keep your head when all about you
    Are losing theirs and blaming it on you:
If you can trust yourself when all men doubt you,
    But make allowance for their doubting too;
If you can wait and not be tired by waiting,
    Or being lied about, don't deal in lies,
Or being hated don't give way to hating,
    And yet don't look too good, nor talk too wise:

If you can dream—and not make dreams your master;
    If you can think—and not make thoughts your aim;
If you can meet with Triumph and Disaster
    And treat those two impostors just the same;
If you can bear to hear the truth you've spoken
    Twisted by knaves to make a trap for fools,
Or watch the things you gave your life to broken,
    And stoop and build 'em up with worn-out tools:

If you can make one heap of all your winnings
  And risk it on one turn of pitch-and-toss,
And lose, and start again at your beginnings
  And never breathe a word about your loss;
If you can force your heart and nerve and sinew
  To serve your turn long after they are gone,
And so hold on when there is nothing in you
    Except the Will which says to them: 'Hold on!'

If you can talk with crowds and keep your virtue,
    Or walk with Kings—nor lose the common touch,
If neither foes nor loving friends can hurt you,
    If all men count with you, but none too much;
If you can fill the unforgiving minute
    With sixty seconds' worth of distance run,
Yours is the Earth and everything that's in it,
    And—which is more—you'll be a Man, my son!

109   THE DONKEY

G. K. Chesterton
(1874-1936)

When fishes flew and forests walked
  And figs grew upon thorn,
Some moment when the moon was blood
  Then surely I was born.

With monstrous head and sickening cry
  And ears like errant wings,
The devil's walking parody
  On all four-footed things.

The tattered outlaw of the earth,
  Of ancient crooked will;
Starve, scourge, deride me: I am dumb,
  I keep my secret still.

Fools! For I also had my hour;
    One far fierce hour and sweet:
There was a shout about my ears,
    And palms before my feet.

110 LOVELIEST OF TREES

A. E. Housman

(1859-1936)

Loveliest of trees, the cherry now
Is hung with bloom along the bough,
And stands about the woodland ride
Wearing white for Eastertide.

Now, of my threescore years and ten,
Twenty will not come again,
And take from seventy springs a score,
It only leaves me fifty more.

And since to look at things in bloom
Fifty springs are little room,
About the woodlands I will go
To see the cherry hung with snow.

111 WHEN I WAS ONE-AND-TWENTY

A. E. Housman

When I was one-and-twenty
    I heard a wise man say,
'Give crowns and pounds and guineas
    But not your heart away;
Give pearls away and rubies,
    But keep your fancy free.'
But I was one-and-twenty,
    No use to talk to me.

When I was one-and-twenty
I heard him say again,
'The heart out of the bosom
Was never given in vain;
'Tis paid with sighs a plenty
And sold for endless rue.'
And I am two-and-twenty,
And oh, 'tis true, 'tis true.

112   VITAI LAMPADA

Sir Henry Newbolt
(1862-1938)

There's a breathless hush in the Close to-night—
Ten to make and the match to win—
A bumping pitch and a blinding light,
An hour to play and the last man in.
And it's not for the sake of a ribboned coat,
Or for the selfish hope of a season's fame,
But his Captain's hand on his shoulder smote—
'Play up! play up! and play the game!'

The sand of the desert is sodden red,—
Red with the wreck of a square that broke;—
The Gatling's jammed and the Colonel dead,
And the regiment blind with dust and smoke.
The river of death has brimmed his banks,
And England's far, and Honour a name,
But the voice of a schoolboy rallies the ranks:
'Play up! play up! and play the game!'

This is the word that year by year,
    While in her place the School is set,
Every one of her sons must hear,
    And none that hears it dare forget.
This they all with a joyful mind
    Bear through life like a torch in flame,
And falling fling to the host behind—
    'Play up! play up! and play the game!'

113   ADMIRALS ALL

Sir Henry Newbolt

Effingham, Grenville, Raleigh, Drake,
    Here's to the bold and free!
Benbow, Collingwood, Byron, Blake,
    Hail to the Kings of the Sea!
Admirals all, for England's sake,
    Honour be yours and fame!
And honour, as long as waves shall break,
    To Nelson's peerless name!

    Admirals all, for England's sake,
        Honour be yours and fame!
    And honour, as long as waves shall break,
        To Nelson's peerless name!

Essex was fretting in Cadiz Bay
    With the galleons fair in sight;
Howard at last must give him his way,
    And the word was passed to fight.
Never was schoolboy gayer than he,
    Since holidays first began:
He tossed his bonnet to wind and sea,
    And under the guns he ran.

Drake nor devil nor Spaniard feared,
    Their cities he put to the sack;
He singed His Catholic Majesty's beard,
    And harried his ships to wrack.
He was playing at Plymouth a rubber of bowls
    When the great Armada came;
But he said, 'They must wait their turn, good souls,'
    And he stooped, and finished the game.

Fifteen sail were the Dutchmen bold,
    Duncan he had but two:
But he anchored them fast where the Texel shoaled
    And his colours aloft he flew.
'I've taken the depth to a fathom,' he cried,
    'And I'll sink with a right good will,
For I know when we're all of us under the tide
    My flag will be fluttering still.'

Splinters were flying above, below,
    When Nelson sailed the Sound:
'Mark you, I wouldn't be elsewhere now,'
    Said he, 'for a thousand pound!'
The Admiral's signal bade him fly,
    But he wickedly wagged his head,
He clapped the glass to his sightless eye,
    And 'I'm damned if I see it,' he said.

Admirals all, they said their say
    (The echoes are ringing still);
Admirals all, they went their way
    To the haven under the hill.
But they left us a kingdom none can take,
    The realm of the circling sea,
To be ruled by the rightful sons of Blake
    And the Rodneys yet to be.

    Admirals all, for England's sake,
        Honour be yours and fame!
    And honour, as long as waves shall break,
        To Nelson's peerless name!

Sir Henry Newbolt

Drake he's in his hammock an' a thousand mile away,
  (Capten, art tha sleepin' there below?),
Slung atween the round-shot in Nombre Dios Bay,
  And dreamin' arl the time o' Plymouth Hoe.
Yarnder lumes the Island, yarnder lie the ships,
  Wi' sailor lads a-dancin' heel-an-toe,
An' the shore-lights flashin', an' the night-tide dashin',
  He sees et arl so plainly as he saw et long ago.

Drake he was a Devon man, an' ruled the Devon seas,
  (Capten, art tha sleepin' there below?),
Rovin' tho' his death fell, he went wi' heart at ease,
  An' dreamin' arl the time o' Plymouth Hoe.
'Take my drum to England, hang et by the shore,
  Strike et when your powder's runnin' low;
If the Dons sight Devon, I'll quit the port o' Heaven,
  An' drum them up the Channel as we drummed them
                                           long ago.'

Drake he's in his hammock till the great Armadas come,
  (Capten, art tha sleepin' there below?),
Slung atween the round-shot, listenin' for the drum,
  An' dreamin' arl the time o' Plymouth Hoe.
Call him on the deep sea, call him up the Sound,
  Call him when ye sail to meet the foe;
Where the old trade's plyin' an' the old flag flyin'
  They shall find him ware an' wakin', as they found
                                           him long ago!

115   HE FELL AMONG THIEVES

Sir Henry Newbolt

'Ye have robbed,' said he, 'ye have slaughtered and made
              an end,
 Take your ill-got plunder, and bury the dead:
What will ye more of your guest and sometime friend?'
 'Blood for our blood,' they said.

He laughed: 'If one may settle the score for five,
 I am ready; but let the reckoning stand till day:
I have loved the sunlight as dearly as any alive.'
 'You shall die at dawn,' said they.

He flung his empty revolver down the slope,
 He climbed alone to the Eastward edge of the trees;
All night long in a dream untroubled of hope
 He brooded, clasping his knees.

He did not hear the monotonous roar that fills
 The ravine where the Yassin river sullenly flows;
He did not see the starlight on the Laspur hills,
 Or the far Afghan snows.

He saw the April noon on his books aglow,
 The wistaria trailing in at the window wide;
He heard his father's voice from the terrace below
 Calling him down to ride.

He saw the gray little church across the park,
 The mounds that hid the loved and honoured dead;
The Norman arch, the chancel softly dark,
 The brasses black and red.

He saw the School Close, sunny and green,
 The runner beside him, the stand by the parapet wall,
The distant tape, and the crowd roaring between,
 His own name over all.

He saw the dark wainscot and timbered roof,
    The long tables, and the faces merry and keen,
The College Eight and their trainer dining aloof,
    The Dons on the dais serene.

He watched the liner's stem ploughing the foam,
    He felt her trembling speed and the thrash of her screw;
He heard the passengers' voices talking of home,
    He saw the flag she flew.

And now it was dawn. He rose strong on his feet,
    And strode to his ruined camp below the wood;
He drank the breath of the morning cool and sweet;
    His murderers round him stood.

Light on the Laspur hills was broadening fast,
    The blood-red snow-peaks chilled to a dazzling white;
He turned, and saw the golden circle at last,
    Cut by the Eastern height.

'O glorious Life, Who dwellest in earth and sun,
    I have lived, I praise and adore Thee.'
        A sword swept.
Over the pass the voices one by one
    Faded, and the hill slept.

116   THE LAKE ISLE OF
INNISFREE

W. B. Yeats
(1865-1939)

I will arise and go now, and go to Innisfree,
And a small cabin build there, of clay and wattles made;
Nine bean rows will I have there, a hive for the honey bee,
    And live alone in the bee-loud glade.

And I shall have some peace there, for peace comes
                                      dropping slow,
Dropping from the veils of the morning to where the
                                      cricket sings;
There midnight's all a-glimmer, and noon a purple glow,
    And evening full of the linnet's wings.

I will arise and go now, for always night and day
I hear lake water lapping with low sounds by the shore;
While I stand on the roadway, or on the pavements gray,
    I hear it in the deep heart's core.

117   LEISURE

W. H. Davies
(1871-1940)

What is this life if, full of care,
We have no time to stand and stare?

No time to stand beneath the boughs
And stare as long as sheep or cows;

No time to see, when woods we pass,
Where squirrels hide their nuts in grass;

No time to see, in broad daylight,
Streams full of stars, like skies at night;

No time to turn at Beauty's glance,
And watch her feet, how they can dance;

No time to wait till her mouth can
Enrich that smile her eyes began?

A poor life this if, full of care,
We have no time to stand and stare.

*FOR THE FALLEN

Laurence Binyon
(1869-1943)

With proud thanksgiving, a mother for her children,
England mourns for her dead across the sea.
Flesh of her flesh they were, spirit of her spirit,
Fallen in the cause of the free.

Solemn the drums thrill: Death august and royal
Sings sorrow up into immortal spheres.
There is music in the midst of desolation
And a glory that shines upon our tears.

They went with songs to the battle, they were young,
Straight of limb, true of eye, steady and aglow.
They were staunch to the end against odds uncounted,
They fell with their faces to the foe.

They shall grow not old, as we that are left grow old:
Age shall not weary them, nor the years condemn.
At the going down of the sun and in the morning
We will remember them.

They mingle not with their laughing comrades again;
They sit no more at familiar tables of home;
They have no lot in our labour of the day-time:
They sleep beyond England's foam.

But where our desires are and our hopes profound,
Felt as a well-spring that is hidden from sight,
To the innermost heart of their own land they are known
As the stars are known to the Night.

As the stars that shall be bright when we are dust,
Moving in marches upon the heavenly plain,
As the stars that are starry in the time of our darkness,
To the end, to the end, they remain.

119 THE SOUTH COUNTRY

Hilaire Belloc
(1870-1953)

When I am living in the Midlands
    That are sodden and unkind,
I light my lamp in the evening:
    My work is left behind;
And the great hills of the South Country
    Come back into my mind.

The great hills of the South Country
    They stand along the sea;
And it's there, walking in the high woods,
    That I could wish to be,
And the men that were boys when I was a boy
    Walking along with me.

The men that live in North England
    I saw them for a day:
Their hearts are set upon the waste fells,
    Their skies are fast and grey;
From their castle-walls a man may see
    The mountains far away.

The men that live in West England
    They see the Severn strong,
A-rolling on rough water brown
    Light aspen leaves along.
They have the secret of the Rocks,
    And the oldest kind of song.

But the men that live in the South Country
    Are the kindest and most wise,
They get their laughter from the loud surf,
    And the faith in their happy eyes
Comes surely from our Sister the Spring
    When over the sea she flies;
The violets suddenly bloom at her feet,
    She blesses us with surprise.

I never get between the pines
    But I smell the Sussex air;
Nor I never come on a belt of sand
    But my home is there.
And along the sky the line of the Downs
    So noble and so bare.

A lost thing could I never find,
    Nor a broken thing mend:
And I fear I shall be all alone
    When I get towards the end.
Who will there be to comfort me
    Or who will be my friend?

I will gather and carefully make my friends
    Of the men of the Sussex Weald,
They watch the stars from silent folds,
    They stiffly plough the field.
By them and the God of the South Country
    My poor soul shall be healed.

If I ever become a rich man,
    Or if ever I grow to be old,
I will build a house with deep thatch
    To shelter me from the cold,
And there shall the Sussex songs be sung
    And the story of Sussex told.

I will hold my house in the high wood
    Within a walk of the sea,
And the men that were boys when I was a boy
    Shall sit and drink with me.

ROMANCE

W. J. Turner
(1889-1946)

When I was but thirteen or so
  I went into a golden land,
Chimborazo, Cotopaxi
  Took me by the hand.

My father died, my brother too,
  They passed like fleeting dreams.
I stood where Popocatapetl
  In the sunlight gleams.

I dimly heard the Master's voice
  And boys far-off at play,
Chimborazo, Cotopaxi
  Had stolen me away.

I walked in a great golden dream
  To and fro from school—
Shining Popocatapetl
  The dusty streets did rule.

I walked home with a gold dark boy
  And never a word I'd say,
Chimborazo, Cotopaxi
  Had taken my speech away:

I gazed entranced upon his face
  Fairer than any flower—
O shining Popocatapetl,
  It was thy magic hour.

The houses, people, traffic seemed
  Thin fading dreams by day,
Chimborazo, Cotopaxi,
  They had stolen my soul away!

121   THE HIGHWAYMAN

Alfred Noyes
(1880-1958)

PART ONE

The wind was a torrent of darkness among the gusty trees,
The moon was a ghostly galleon tossed upon cloudy seas,
The road was a ribbon of moonlight over the purple moor,
And the highwayman came riding—
        Riding—riding—
The highwayman came riding, up to the old inn-door.

He'd a French cocked-hat on his forehead, a bunch of lace
                        at his chin,
A coat of claret velvet, and breeches of brown doe-skin;
They fitted with never a wrinkle: his boots were up to the
                        thigh!
And he rode with a jewelled twinkle,
        His pistol butts a-twinkle,
His rapier hilt a-twinkle, under the jewelled sky.

Over the cobbles he clattered and clashed in the dark
                        inn-yard,
And he tapped with his whip on the shutters, but all was
                        locked and barred;
He whistled a tune to the window, and who should be
                        waiting there
But the landlord's black-eyed daughter,
        Bess, the landlord's daughter,
Plaiting a dark red love-knot into her long black hair.

And dark in the dark old inn-yard a stable-wicket creaked
Where Tom the ostler listened; his face was white and
                        peaked;
His eyes were hollows of madness, his hair like mouldy hay,
But he loved the landlord's daughter,
        The landlord's red-lipped daughter.
Dumb as a dog he listened, and he heard the robber say—

'One kiss, my bonny sweetheart, I'm after a prize to-night,
But I shall be back with the yellow gold before the morning
light;
Yet, if they press me sharply, and harry me through the day,
Then look for me by moonlight,
Watch for me by moonlight,
I'll come to thee by moonlight, though hell should bar
the way.'

He rose upright in the stirrups; he scarce could reach her
hand,
But she loosen'd her hair i' the casement! His face burnt
like a brand
As the black cascade of perfume came tumbling over his breast;
And he kissed its waves in the moonlight,
(Oh, sweet black waves in the moonlight!)
Then he tugged at his rein in the moonlight, and galloped
away to the West.

PART TWO

He did not come in the dawning; he did not come at noon;
And out o' the tawny sunset, before the rise o' the moon,
When the road was a gipsy's ribbon, looping the purple
moor,
A red-coat troop came marching—
Marching—marching—
King George's men came marching, up to the old inn-door.

They said no word to the landlord, they drank his ale
instead,
But they gagged his daughter and bound her to the foot of
her narrow bed;
Two of them knelt at her casement, with muskets at their
side!
There was death at every window;
And hell at one dark window;
For Bess could see, through her casement, the road that *he*
would ride.

154

They had tied her up to attention, with many a sniggering jest;
They had bound a musket beside her, with the barrel
                                  beneath her breast!
'Now keep good watch!' and they kissed her.
            She heard the dead man say—
Look for me by moonlight;
            Watch for me by moonlight;
I'll come to thee by moonlight, though hell should bar the way!

She twisted her hands behind her; but all the knots held
                                              good!
She writhed her hands till her fingers were wet with sweat
                                          or blood!
They stretched and strained in the darkness, and the hours
                                  crawled by like years,
Till now, on the stroke of midnight,
            Cold, on the stroke of midnight,
The tip of one finger touched it!   The trigger at last was hers!

The tip of one finger touched it; she strove no more for
                                          the rest!
Up, she stood to attention, with the barrel beneath her
                                          breast.
She would not risk their hearing; she would not strive again;
For the road lay bare in the moonlight;
            Blank and bare in the moonlight;
And the blood of her veins in the moonlight throbbed to
                                  her lover's refrain.

Tlot-tlot; tlot-tlot! Had they heard it? The horse-hoofs
                                  ringing clear;
Tlot-tlot; tlot-tlot, in the distance? Were they deaf that
                                  they did not hear?
Down the ribbon of moonlight, over the brow of the hill,
The highwayman came riding,
            Riding, riding!
The red-coats looked to their priming! She stood up,
                                  straight and still!

155

Tlot-tlot, in the frosty silence! *Tlot-tlot*, in the echoing night!
Nearer he came and nearer! Her face was like a light!
Her eyes grew wide for a moment, she drew one last deep
Then her finger moved in the moonlight,   breath,
        Her musket shattered the moonlight,
Shattered her breast in the moonlight and warned him—
                            with her death.

He turned, he spurred to the Westward; he did not know
                            who stood
Bowed, with her head o'er the musket, drenched with her
                            own red blood!
Not till the dawn he heard it, and slowly blanched to hear
How Bess, the landlord's daughter,
        The landlord's black-eyed daughter,
Had watched for her love in the moonlight, and died in
                            the darkness there.

Back, he spurred like a madman, shrieking a curse to the sky,
With the white road smoking behind him and his rapier
                            brandished high!
Blood-red were his spurs i' the golden noon; wine-red was
                            his velvet coat;
When they shot him down on the highway,
        Down like a dog on the highway,
And he lay in his blood on the highway, with a bunch of
                            lace at his throat.

And still of a winter's night, they say, when the wind is in
                            the trees,
When the moon is a ghostly galleon tossed upon cloudy seas,
When the road is a ribbon of moonlight over the purple moor,
A highwayman comes riding—
        Riding—riding—
A highwayman comes riding, up to the old inn-door.

Over the cobbles he clatters and clangs in the dark inn-yard;
And he taps with his whip on the shutters, but all is locked
                            and barred;
He whistles a tune to the window, and who should be waiting
But the landlord's black-eyed daughter,   *there*
        Bess, the landlord's daughter,
Plaiting a dark red love-knot into her long black hair.

THE LISTENERS

Walter de la Mare

(*1873-1956*)

'Is there anybody there?' said the Traveller,
    Knocking on the moonlit door;
And his horse in the silence champed the grasses
    Of the forest's ferny floor;
And a bird flew up out of the turret,
    Above the Traveller's head:
And he smote upon the door again a second time;
    'Is there anybody there?' he said.
But no one descended to the Traveller;
    No head from the leaf-fringed sill
Leaned over and looked into his grey eyes,
    Where he stood perplexed and still.
But only a host of phantom listeners
    That dwelt in the lone house then
Stood listening in the quiet of the moonlight
    To that voice from the world of men:
Stood thronging the faint moonbeams on the dark stair,
    That goes down to the empty hall,
Hearkening in an air stirred and shaken
    By the lonely Traveller's call.
And he felt in his heart their strangeness,
    Their stillness answering his cry,
While his horse moved, cropping the dark turf,
    'Neath the starred and leafy sky;
For he suddenly smote on the door, even
    Louder, and lifted his head:—
'Tell them I came, and no one answered,
    That I kept my word,' he said.
Never the least stir made the listeners,
    Though every word he spake
Fell echoing through the shadowiness of the still house
    From the one man left awake:
Ay, they heard his foot upon the stirrup,
    And the sound of iron on stone,
And how the silence surged softly backward,
    When the plunging hoofs were gone.

123　　　　**THE SCARECROW**

Walter de la Mare

All winter through I bow my head
　　Beneath the driving rain;
The North wind powders me with snow
　　And blows me black again;
At midnight under a maze of stars
　　I flame with glittering rime,
And stand, above the stubble, stiff
　　As mail at morning-prime.
But when that child, called Spring, and all
　　His host of children, come,
Scattering their buds and dew upon
　　These acres of my home,
Some rapture in my rags awakes;
　　I lift void eyes and scan
The skies for crows, those ravening foes
　　Of my strange master, Man.
I watch him striding lank behind
　　His clashing team, and know
Soon will the wheat swish body high
　　Where once lay sterile snow;
Soon shall I gaze across a sea
　　Of sun-begotten grain,
Which my unflinching watch hath sealed
　　For harvest once again.

124　　　　MRS.　REECE　LAUGHS

Martin Armstrong
(1882 —)

Laughter, with us, is no great undertaking,
A sudden wave that breaks and dies in breaking.
Laughter, with Mrs. Reece, is much less simple:
It germinates, it spreads, dimple by dimple,
From small beginnings, things of easy girth,
To formidable redundancies of mirth.

Clusters of subterranean chuckles rise,
And presently the circles of her eyes
Close into slits, and all the woman heaves,
As a great elm with all its mounds of leaves
Wallows before the storm.   From hidden sources
A mustering of blind volcanic forces
Takes her and shakes her till she sobs and gapes.
Then all that load of bottled mirth escapes
In one wild crow, a lifting of huge hands,
And creaking stays, and visage that expands
In scarlet ridge and furrow.   Thence collapse,
A hanging head, a feeble hand that flaps
An apron-end to stir an air and waft
A steaming face.   And Mrs. Reece has laughed.

125   NIGHT MAIL

W. II. Auden
(1907 —)

This is the night mail crossing the border,
Bringing the cheque and the postal order,
Letters for the rich, letters for the poor,
The shop at the corner and the girl next door.
Pulling up Beattock, a steady climb—
The gradient's against her, but she's on time.

Past cotton grass and moorland boulder
Shovelling white steam over her shoulder,
Snorting noisily as she passes
Silent miles of wind-bent grasses.
Birds turn their heads as she approaches,
Stare from the bushes at her blank-faced coaches.
Sheep dogs cannot turn her course,
They slumber on with paws across.
In the farm she passes no one wakes,
But a jug in the bedroom gently shakes.

Dawn freshens, the climb is done.
Down towards Glasgow she descends
Towards the steam tugs yelping down the glade of cranes,
Towards the fields of apparatus, the furnaces
Set on the dark plain like gigantic chessmen.
All Scotland waits for her:
In the dark glens, beside the pale-green lochs,
Men long for news.

Letters of thanks, letters from banks,
Letters of joy from girl and boy,
Receipted bills and invitations
To inspect new stock or visit relations,
And applications for situations
And timid lovers' declarations
And gossip, gossip from all the nations,
News circumstantial, news financial,
Letters with holiday snaps to enlarge in,
Letters with faces scrawled in the margin,
Letters from uncles, cousins and aunts,
Letters to Scotland from the South of France,
Letters of condolence to Highlands and Lowlands,
Notes from overseas to Hebrides—
Written on paper of every hue,
The pink, the violet, the white and the blue,
The chatty, the catty, the boring, adoring,
The cold and official and the heart's outpouring,
Clever, stupid, short and long,
The typed and the printed and the spelt all wrong.

Thousands are still asleep
Dreaming of terrifying monsters,
Or a friendly tea beside the band at Cranston's or Crawford's:
Asleep in working Glasgow, asleep in well-set Edinburgh,
Asleep in granite Aberdeen.
They continue their dreams;
But shall wake soon and long for letters,
And none will hear the postman's knock
Without a quickening of the heart,
For who can hear and feel himself forgotten?

126 MACAVITY: THE MYSTERY CAT

T. S. Eliot
(1888 —)

Macavity's a Mystery Cat: he's called the Hidden Paw—
For he's the master criminal who can defy the Law.
He's the bafflement of Scotland Yard, the Flying Squad's
despair:
For when they reach the scene of crime—*Macavity's not*
there!

Macavity, Macavity, there's no-one like Macavity,
He's broken every human law, he breaks the law of gravity.
His powers of levitation would make a fakir stare,
And when you reach the scene of crime—*Macavity's not*
there!
You may seek him in the basement, you may look up in
the air—
But I tell you once and once again, *Macavity's not there!*

Macavity's a ginger cat, he's very tall and thin;
You would know him if you saw him, for his eyes are
sunken in.
His brow is deeply lined with thought, his head is highly
domed;
His coat is dusty from neglect, his whiskers are uncombed.
He sways his head from side to side, with movements like
a snake;
And when you think he's half asleep, he's always wide awake.

Macavity, Macavity, there's no-one like Macavity,
For he's a fiend in feline shape, a monster of depravity.
You may meet him in a by-street, you may see him in the
square—
But when a crime's discovered, then *Macavity's not there!*

He's outwardly respectable. (They say he cheats at cards.)
And his footprints are not found in any file of Scotland
Yard's.
And when the larder's looted, or the jewel-case is rifled,
Or when the milk is missing, or another Peke's been stifled,
Or the greenhouse glass is broken, and the trellis past repair—
Ay, there's the wonder of the thing! *Macavity's not there!*

And when the Foreign Office find a Treaty's gone astray,
Or the Admiralty lose some plans and drawings by the way,
There may be a scrap of paper in the hall or on the stair—
But it's useless to investigate—*Macavity's not there!*
And when the loss has been disclosed, the Secret Service say:
'It *must* have been Macavity!'—but he's a mile away.
You'll be sure to find him resting, or a-licking of his thumbs,
Or engaged in doing complicated long division sums.

Macavity, Macavity, there's no-one like Macavity,
There never was a Cat of such deceitfulness and suavity.
He always has an alibi, and one or two to spare:
At whatever time the deed took place—MACAVITY
                              WASN'T THERE!
And they say that all the Cats whose wicked deeds are
                              widely known
(I might mention Mungojerrie, I might mention Griddlebone)
Are nothing more than agents for the Cat who all the time
Just controls their operations: the Napoleon of Crime!

127   JOURNEY OF THE MAGI

T. S. Eliot

'A cold coming we had of it,
Just the worst time of the year
For a journey, and such a long journey:
The ways deep and the weather sharp,
The very dead of winter.'
And the camels galled, sore-footed, refractory,
Lying down in the melting snow.   ·
There were times we regretted
The summer palaces on slopes, the terraces,
And the silken girls bringing sherbet.
Then the camel men cursing and grumbling
And running away, and wanting their liquor and women,
And the night-fires going out, and the lack of shelters,
And the cities hostile and the towns unfriendly
And the villages dirty and charging high prices:
A hard time we had of it.

At the end we preferred to travel all night,
Sleeping in snatches,
With the voices singing in our ears, saying
That this was all folly.

Then at dawn we came down to a temperate valley,
Wet, below the snow line, smelling of vegetation;
With a running stream and a water-mill beating the darkness,
And three trees on the low sky,
And an old white horse galloped away in the meadow.
Then we came to a tavern with vine-leaves over thc lintel,
Six hands at an open door dicing for pieces of silver,
And feet kicking the empty wine-skins.
But there was no information, and so we continued
And arrived at evening, not a moment too soon
Finding the place: it was (you may say) satisfactory.

All this was a long time ago I remember,
And I would do it again, but set down
This set down
This: were we led all that way for
Birth or Death? There was a Birth certainly,
We had evidence and no doubt. I had seen birth and death,
But had thought they were different; this Birth was
Hard and bitter agony for us, like Death, our death.
We returned to our places, these Kingdoms,
But no longer at ease here, in the old dispensation,
With an alien people clutching their gods.
I should be glad of another death.

128   FLANNAN ISLE

W. W. Gibson
(1878 —)

'Though three men dwell on Flannan Isle
To keep the lamp alight,
As we steer'd under the lee, we caught
No glimmer through the night!'

A passing ship at dawn had brought
The news; and quickly we set sail,
To find out what strange thing might ail
The keepers of the deep-sea light.

The winter day broke blue and bright,
With glancing sun and glancing spray,
As o'er the swell our boat made way,
As gallant as a gull in flight.

But, as we near'd the lonely Isle
And looked up at the naked height;
And saw the lighthouse towering white,
With blinded lantern, that all night
Had never shot a spark
Of comfort through the dark,
So ghostly in the cold sunlight
It seem'd, that we were struck the while
With wonder all too dread for words.

And, as into the tiny creek
We stole beneath the hanging crag,
We saw three queer, black, ugly birds—
Too big, by far, in my belief,
For guillemot or shag—
Like seamen sitting bolt-upright
Upon a half-tide reef:
But, as we near'd, they plunged from sight,
Without a sound, or spurt of white.

And still too mazed to speak,
We landed; and made fast the boat;
And climb'd the track in single file,
Each wishing he was safe afloat,
On any sea, however far,
So it be far from Flannan Isle:
And still we seem'd to climb, and climb,
As though we'd lost all count of time,
And so must climb for evermore.
Yet, all too soon, we reached the door—
The black, sun-blister'd lighthouse-door,
That gaped for us ajar.

As, on the threshold, for a spell,
We paused, we seem'd to breathe the smell
Of limewash and of tar,
Familiar as our daily breath,
As though 'twere some strange scent of death:
And so, yet wondering, side by side,
We stood a moment, still tongue-tied:
And each with black foreboding eyed
The door, ere we should fling it wide,
To leave the sunlight for the gloom:
Till, plucking courage up, at last,
Hard on each other's heels we pass'd
Into the living-room.

Yet, as we crowded through the door,
We only saw a table, spread
For dinner, meat and cheese and bread;
But all untouch'd; and no one there:
As though, when they sat down to eat,
Ere they could even taste,
Alarm had come; and they in haste
Had risen and left the bread and meat:
For at the table-head a chair
Lay tumbled on the floor.
We listen'd; but we only heard
The feeble cheeping of a bird
That starved upon its perch:
And, listening still, without a word,
We set about our hopeless search.

We hunted high, we hunted low,
And soon ransack'd the empty house;
Then o'er the Island, to and fro,
We ranged, to listen and to look
In every cranny, cleft or nook
That might have hid a bird or mouse:
But, though we search'd from shore to shore,
We found no sign in any place:
And soon again stood face to face
Before the gaping door:
And stole into the room once more
As frighten'd children steal.

Aye: though we hunted high and low,
And hunted everywhere,
Of the three men's fate we found no trace
Of any kind in any place,
But a door ajar, and an untouch'd meal,
And an overtoppled chair.

And, as we listen'd in the gloom
Of that forsaken living-room—
A chill clutch on our breath—
We thought how ill-chance came to all
Who kept the Flannan Light:
And how the rock had been the death
Of many a likely lad:
How six had come to a sudden end,
And three had gone stark mad:
And one whom we'd all known as friend
Had leapt from the lantern one still night,
And fallen dead by the lighthouse wall:
And long we thought
On the three we sought,
And of what might yet befall.

Like curs a glance has brought to heel,
We listen'd, flinching there:
And look'd and look'd, on the untouch'd **meal**
And the overtoppled chair.

We seem'd to stand for an endless while,
Though still no word was said,
Three men alive on Flannan Isle
Who thought on three men dead.

129 TIME, YOU OLD GIPSY MAN

Ralph Hodgson
(1871 —)

Time, you old gipsy man,
 Will you not stay,
Put up your caravan
 Just for one day?

All things I'll give you,
Will you be my guest,
Bells for your jennet
Of silver the best,
Goldsmiths shall beat you
A great golden ring,
Peacocks shall bow to you,
Little boys sing,
Oh, and sweet girls will
Festoon you with may,
Time, you old gipsy,
Why hasten away?

Last week in Babylon,
Last night in Rome,
Morning, and in the crush
Under Paul's dome;
Under Paul's dial
You tighten your rein—
Only a moment,
And off once again;
Off to some city
Now blind in the womb,
Off to another
Ere that's in the tomb.

Time, you old gipsy man,
 Will you not stay,
Put up your caravan
 Just for one day?

130   CARGOES

John Masefield
(1878 —)

Quinquireme of Nineveh from distant Ophir
Rowing home to haven in sunny Palestine,
With a cargo of ivory,
And apes and peacocks,
Sandalwood, cedarwood, and sweet white wine.

Stately Spanish galleon coming from the Isthmus,
Dipping through the tropics by the palm-green shores,
With a cargo of diamonds,
Emeralds, amethysts,
Topazes, and cinnamon, and gold moidores.

Dirty British coaster with a salt-caked smoke stack
Butting through the Channel in the mad March days,
With a cargo of Tyne coal,
Road-rail, pig-lead,
Firewood, iron-ware, and cheap tin trays.

131   SEA-FEVER

John Masefield

I must go down to the sea again, to the lonely sea and the sky,
And all I ask is a tall ship and a star to steer her by;
And the wheel's kick and the wind's song and the white
                          sail's shaking,
And a grey mist on the sea's face, and a grey dawn breaking.

I must go down to the seas again, for the call of the
                          running tide
Is a wild call and a clear call that may not be denied;
And all I ask is a windy day with the white clouds flying,
And the flung spray and the blown spume, and the sea-gulls
                          crying.

I must go down to the seas again, to the vagrant gipsy life,
To the gull's way and the whale's way where the wind's
                                                    like a whetted knife;
And all I ask is a merry yarn from a laughing fellow-rover,
And quiet sleep and a sweet dream when the long trick's over.

132 ROADWAYS

John Masefield

One road leads to London,
    One road leads to Wales,
My road leads me seawards
    To the white dipping sails.

One road leads to the river,
    As it goes singing slow;
My road leads to shipping,
    Where the bronzed sailors go.

Leads me, lures me, calls me
    To salt green tossing sea;
A road without earth's road-dust
    Is the right road for me.

A wet road heaving, shining,
    And wild with seagulls' cries,
A mad salt sea-wind blowing
    The salt spray in my eyes.

My road calls me, lures me
    West, east, south, and north;
Most roads lead men homewards,
    My road leads me forth,

To add more miles to the tally
    Of grey miles left behind,
In quest of that one beauty
    God put me here to find.

FIRST LINES OF POEMS

	Page
'A cold coming we had of it, (127)	162
A snake came to my water-trough (104)	132
A wet sheet and a flowing sea, (46)	56
Abou Ben Adhem (may his tribe increase!) (59)	75
All along the backwater, (105)	135
All winter through I bow my head (123)	158
And did those feet in ancient time (41)	50
Behold her, single in the field, (56)	72
Blow, blow, thou winter wind, (4)	15
Break, break, break, (83)	104
Christmas Eve, and twelve of the clock. (102)	130
Cold in the earth—and the deep snow piled above thee, (54)	71
Come away, come away, death, (6)	16
Come live with me, and be my love, (1)	13
Does the road wind up-hill all the way? (86)	107
Drake he's in his hammock an' a thousand mile away, (114)	145
Drink to me only with thine eyes, (10)	19
Earth has not anything to show more fair: (55)	72
Effingham, Grenville, Raleigh, Drake, (113)	143
Fair Daffodils, we weep to see (16)	24
Fear death?—to feel the fog in my throat, (75)	94
Fear no more the heat o' the sun, (7)	17
Gather ye rose-buds while ye may, (15)	23
Glory be to God for dappled things— (76)	95
Go, lovely Rose! (19)	26
God of our fathers, known of old, (107)	138
Good people all, of every sort, (23)	29
Hail to thee, blithe Spirit! (34)	42
Half a league, half a league, (79)	97
He clasps the crag with crooked hands; (82)	104
He thought he saw an Elephant, (90)	115
How do I love thee? Let me count the ways. (60)	76
How happy is he born or taught (11)	20
How sleep the brave who sink to rest (21)	27
I bring fresh showers for the thirsting flowers, (33)	40
I come from haunts of coot and hern, (84)	105
I have come to the borders of sleep, (99)	128
I have seen old ships sail like swans asleep (97)	126
I met a traveller from an antique land (32)	39
I must go down to the sea again, to the lonely sea and the sky, (131)	168
I remember, I remember, (53)	70
I sprang to the stirrup, and Joris, and he; (73)	90
I wander'd lonely as a cloud (57)	73
I will arise and go now, and go to Innisfree, (116)	147
If I should die, think only this of me: (96)	125
If you can keep your head when all about you (108)	139
In Xanadu did Kubla Khan (45)	55
'Is there anybody there?' said the Traveller, (122)	157
Is there for honest Poverty (25)	31
It was a lover and his lass, (8)	18

	Page
It was a summer evening, (48)	59
King and Queen of the Pelicans we; (70)	86
Laughter, with us, is no great undertaking, (124)	158
Little Lamb, who made thee? (39)	49
Little trotty wagtail, he went in the rain, (62)	77
Loveliest of trees, the cherry now (110)	141
Macavity's a Mystery Cat: he's called the Hidden Paw— (126)	161
Much have I travell'd in the realms of gold, (31)	39
My luve is like a red, red rose (24)	30
No stir in the air, no stir in the sea, (47)	57
Not a drum was heard, not a funeral note, (35)	45
O blithe new-comer! I have heard, (58)	74
'O Mary, go and call the cattle home, (66)	81
O, mistress mine, where are you roaming? (5)	16
O say, what is that thing called Light, (20)	26
'O what can ail thee, knight-at-arms, (28)	34
O world invisible, we view thee, (94)	122
O, Young Lochinvar is come out of the west, (42)	51
Oh, to be in England, (72)	90
Old Meg she was a gipsy, (30)	37
On either side the river lie (80)	99
On Linden, when the sun was low, (50)	64
One road leads to London, (132)	169
Out of the night that covers me, (93)	121
Pibroch of Donuil Dhu, (43)	52
Quinquireme of Nineveh from distant Ophir (130)	168
Say not the struggle naught availeth, (61)	76
Seamen three! What men be ye? (64)	79
Season of mists and mellow fruitfulness, (29)	36
She walks in beauty, like the night (38)	48
Should auld acquaintance be forgot, (26)	32
Sing me a song of a lad that is gone, (87)	108
'So the foeman has fired the gate, men of mine; (65)	80
So, we'll go no more a-roving (37)	47
Spring, the sweet Spring, is the year's pleasant king; (2)	14
Strew on her roses, roses, (67)	82
Sunset and evening star, (85)	107
Tell me not, Sweet, I am unkind, (12)	21
That which her slender waist confin'd (18)	25
The Assyrian came down like the wolf on the fold, (36)	46
The glories of our blood and state (14)	23
The mountain sheep are sweeter, (63)	78
The naked earth is warm with spring, (98)	127
The old mayor climbed the belfry tower, (89)	110
The Owl and the Pussy-cat went to sea (71)	89
The sea is calm to-night. (68)	82
The splendour falls on castle walls (81)	103
The summer and autumn had been so wet, (49)	61
The sun was shining on the sea, (92)	118
The wind was a torrent of darkness among the gusty trees, (121)	153
There's a breathless hush in the Close to-night— (112)	142
They told me, Heraclitus, they told me you were dead, (78)	97

171

	Page
They went to sea in a Sieve, they did, (69)	84
This is the night mail crossing the border, (125)	159
This is the weather the cuckoo likes, (101)	130
'Though three men dwell on Flannan Isle (128)	163
Time, you old gipsy man, (129)	167
Toll for the brave! (27)	33
'Twas on a lofty vase's side, (22)	28
Tyger! Tyger! burning bright (40)	49
Under the greenwood tree, (3)	14
Under the wide and starry sky, (88)	109
Up the airy mountain, (77)	95
What is this life if, full of care, (117)	148
What passing-bells for these who die as cattle? (100)	129
When fishes flew and forests walked (109)	140
When I am living in the Midlands (119)	150
When I consider how my light is spent, (17)	25
When I was but thirteen or so (120)	152
When I was one-and-twenty (111)	141
When Love with unconfined wings (13)	22
When men were all asleep the snow came flying, (103)	131
When pods went pop on the broom, green broom, (95)	123
Who is Silvia? What is she? (9)	19
'Why weep ye by the tide, ladie? (44)	54
With fingers weary and worn, (52)	67
With proud thanksgiving, a mother for her children, (118)	149
'Ye have robbed', said he, 'ye have slaughtered and made an end, (115)	146
Ye Mariners of England (51)	65
'You are old, Father William,' the young man said, (91)	116
You know, we French storm'd Ratisbon: (74)	92
You may talk o' gin and beer (106)	136

172